NUMERACY

KEY STAGE 1: RECEPTION/ P1

SUE ATKINSON

HOPSCOTCH

EDUCATIONAL PUBLISHING

D0332480

Contents

Published by Hopscotch Educational Publishing Ltd,
Althorpe House, Althorpe Street, Leamington Spa CV31 2AU.

© 1999 Hopscotch Educational Publishing

Written by Sue Atkinson
Series design by Blade Communications
Illustrated by Susan Hutchison
Cover illustration by Claire Boyce
Printed by Clintplan, Southam

Sue Atkinson hereby asserts her moral right to be identified as
the author of this work in accordance with the Copyright,
Designs and Patents Act, 1988.

ISBN 1-902239-30-X   372.7 (1505)

ABOUT THE SERIES

Developing Numeracy Skills is a series of books aimed at developing the basic skills of the 'Framework for teaching mathematics'. There is one book for each year from Reception (Scottish Primary 1), through Key Stage 1 to the end of Key Stage 2 (Scottish Primary 7).

The series offers a structured approach which provides detailed lesson plans to teach specific numeracy skills. A unique feature of the series is the provision of differentiated photocopiable activities which are aimed at considerably reducing teacher preparation time.

ABOUT THIS BOOK

This book is for teachers of Reception children and Scottish level P1. It aims to:

◆ give emphasis to those aspects of numeracy that teachers on the National Numeracy Project found to be crucial to raising the standards of numeracy in their classrooms;

◆ support a three-fold structured lesson for maximising learning to raise standards;

◆ support teachers in developing children's flexible methods of calculating;

◆ encourage a wide range of mathematical vocabulary by giving some key questions to ask;

◆ support teachers with a wide range of mental maths questions to develop good mental recall with children.

Throughout the book, bugs and fantasy creatures are used to set maths in a context, but you can adapt the lessons by using your own topic.

(You will find that the content for the Y1/P2 book in this series is structured in a similar way to assist you if you have a mixed age class.)

 ## CHAPTER CONTENT

◆ Overall learning objectives

Each chapter has two lesson plans and the overall learning objectives outline the aims for both lessons and the Further Activities in each chapter.

◆ Assessment focus

This sets out the specific learning objective that you will be able to assess for each individual lesson within the chapter. (See page 4 for more on assessment.)

◆ Resources

This is a list of what you will need to do the lessons.

◆ Oral work and mental calculation

This section is a 'mental maths warm-up' and can have a different learning objective from the main lesson plan. It gives you ideas for how to develop quick mental recall with your children, so keeping key ideas ticking over and giving them the extra practice they need to be confident with mental maths. You can 'mix and match' these to suit your lesson. So you might want to do number bonds to 10 every day for a fortnight, even when your main lesson is about measuring, or you might want to recap something about shape and space on a day when the main lesson is about number, and so on. This section of the lesson is usually about 5 or 10 minutes long.

◆ Starting point: Whole class

This provides ideas for introducing the activity and may include key questions to ask the children so that they can move on to their group task having learned concepts and the vocabulary they will need for the group activities. This starting point is usually about 10 minutes long, depending on the task.

◆ Group activities

This explains the tasks that the children will do. The 'Focus Group' works with you and this group alternates between different ability groups. The section on 'teacher independent groups' gives three tasks that can be done more or less independently of you. Sometimes you might only use two of the three independent tasks because one group is the focus group. The Group 1 tasks are the easiest and the Group 3 tasks the hardest. For Reception children, this section is only 10 or 15 minutes long, depending on the task. Of course, with very young children, many of these tasks need to be structured play, or maths games, so some of these might have slightly different learning objectives from the main lesson. Even with structured play, we cannot expect some children to stick at their task and at this stage, that does not matter. Those children will be learning both from their play and from the whole-class starting point and the plenary session.

 ### Using the differentiated activity sheets

Activity 1 is for the children who are likely to struggle with the content of the lesson and who need a simple task, often with lower numbers than other groups. Activity 2 is for children who seem to have grasped the main ideas during the whole-class starter. Activity 3 is for those who need a more challenging task.

The book symbol at the bottom of some activity pages is for further work to be done in maths books, or on the maths table, but unless you have a helper, you will need to let Reception children play when they finish in order to keep your time with the focus group free of interruptions.

 ### Plenary session

This suggests ideas for a whole-class review to discuss the learning outcomes and gives questions to ask so that children have a chance to reflect on what they have learned and for the teacher to assess. This section is often about 5 or 10 minutes.

 ### Further activities

This is a list of further activities that can be developed from the lessons to give children more experience with the learning objectives.

 ### Extension

These are ideas for how to take children on and give them more difficult tasks.

Support

These are ideas for children who are going to need more support before they have grasped the learning objectives.

 ### The use of calculators

Although children may not be using calculators very much at Key Stage 1, and they will certainly not use them for calculating, they can be very helpful in focusing children onto number patterns, place value and so on. In Reception, calculators are invaluable for teaching number recognition and an understanding of conventional symbols, such as the addition sign. We need them there in the classroom in the play shop and so on, so that the children are free to explore the wonder and excitement of number that can come through using these powerful tools.

 ## GENERIC SHEETS

On pages 90 to 94 there are some generic sheets that give extra help with key skills for Reception children. These sheets can be photocopied with different numbers on them to suit your different groups. Guidance on using them is given in the lesson plans or in the further activities.

 ## ASSESSMENT

At the top of most of the activity sheets there is a row of three small boxes. These link with your assessment of how well the child has grasped the intended learning for that lesson. On page 5 there is a list of the assessment criteria for both lessons for each chapter (for the photocopiable activity sheets these are in italics) and you can use these criteria to decide how well a child has grasped the content of a particular lesson. They should be used as follows:

✦ If they seem not to have grasped the concept, tick the first box.
✦ If there is evidence of the child having learned what you intended, tick the second box.
✦ Tick the third box for children who have a very secure grasp of the lesson and you think can use and apply the concept.

Of course, there will often not be evidence on the sheet that corresponds with your observations of some children's understandings, so you will need to make a note of what they said or did to back up why you ticked a particular box. With young children, recording on sheets is often not going to assess understanding, especially where the lesson is about some acquisition of essential language, for example in Chapter 10 Lesson Two. Assessment is much broader than children's recordings, so your additional annotations are important.

At the end of each half term, flicking through each child's sheets can give you a basis for your teacher assessments, and will help you to plan for your next half term.

In addition to this assessment on the children's sheets, there is a 'brick wall' on page 95 that outlines the basic concepts and skills needed for a secure understanding of counting. Generally, these are the lower bricks on the whole and some other aspects of early number understanding are on higher bricks. (It isn't possible to give an exact order of learning as it varies so much.)

It is absolutely crucial that we do counting every day to give children a firm foundation for later maths work. You can use this brick wall as a flexible resource and photocopy it for each child or group you are concerned

about and who seems not to be counting securely yet. There is plenty of space for you to add other learning objectives, or concepts that the child seems now to understand, or to note their targets for the next half term. As you observe children in mental maths time and playing on the maths table, note their progress and look at the gaps they have and set up relevant structured play. (The brick wall will also be relevant for use with other older children who still are not secure with counting.)

On page 96 there is a blank copy of the brick wall for you to photocopy and use for groups or individuals in any way you choose, maybe putting onto the bricks the learning objectives just for one term for one group, so that you can keep a check on progress. The idea of the brick wall is that it should support your target setting for groups and individuals and that it supports the way your school does assessments.

Reception Assessment Criteria

Chapter 1
+ Can recite number names in order and recognise numbers.
+ *Can understand that the number remains the same however grouped.*

Chapter 2
+ *Can order numbers to 10.*
+ Can compare 2 numbers and say which is more.

Chapter 3
+ Can count a set of objects reliably and tally.
+ *Can count with one number word for each step, and can see the meaning of symbols and record them.*

Chapter 4
+ *Can recite to 20.*
+ Can make reasonable estimates and check by counting.

Chapter 5
+ *Can add and subtract 1.*
+ Can count in 2s at least to 10.

Chapter 6
+ *Can work out how many objects are needed to make a larger number.*
+ Can work out how many less.

Chapter 7
+ Can separate objects into 2 groups then count.
+ *Can combine 2 or 3 groups and count total.*

Chapter 8
+ Can see that putting the larger number first involves fewer steps.
+ *Can recognise addition of doubles.*

Chapter 9
+ Can understand 'take away' and count how many are left.
+ *Can count back and up and see this gives the same answer.*

Chapter 10
+ Can understand they do not need to count from 1 each time.
+ *Can talk about what they do with numbers.*

Chapter 11
+ Can use the language of measures to make direct comparisons, reasonable estimates, then check.
+ *Can use the language of comparison.*

Chapter 12
+ Can place themselves in an appropriate group.
+ *Can use a variety of shapes to make pictures, talking about and counting the shapes.*

Chapter 13
+ *Can recognise, copy and continue repeating patterns.*
+ Can recognise patterns in numbers and predict what would come next.

Chapter 14
+ *Can solve simple mathematical problems related to shape.*
+ Can solve problems related to position, direction and movement.

Counting to 10

◆ Overall learning objectives

- ◆ Recite the number names in order.
- ◆ Count reliably giving just one name to each object (one-to-one correspondence).
- ◆ Number recognition.
- ◆ Conservation of number (reorganising the objects doesn't change the number).

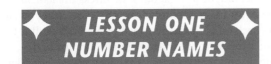

**LESSON ONE
NUMBER NAMES**

◆ Assessment focus

- ◆ Can children recite number names in order to 3/5/10 and above and recognise numbers?

◆ Resources

- ◆ a collection of short sticks
- ◆ number cards 0 – 10
- ◆ a large floor number line 1 – 10
- ◆ stamper pens (available from High Street shops)
- ◆ play dough
- ◆ buttons
- ◆ items for counting
- ◆ old birthday cards with numbers on
- ◆ trays

◆ Oral work and mental calculation

Numbers to 10

- ◆ Start by reciting to 5, then 10 several times.
- ◆ Put number cards in order in front of you. The children come and choose a card and ask the class to hold up that many fingers. Let them come out in turns and say the numbers.

◆ Starting point: Whole class

- ◆ Sit the children in a circle with 6 sticks in front of them laid out in a line. (You might want to do this activity first with 3, 4 or 5 sticks, but even children who can't yet count reliably can learn from using as many as 6.) Children say together:

   One, two, three,
   Four, five six,
   I can count and pick up sticks.

- ◆ They then lift up the sticks one at a time with you counting to 6. This can be repeated several times in different ways. For example, one child picks up just one stick. Say *"Look, Jess just has one stick in her hand. Now all of you pick up just one stick."*
- ◆ Keep repeating the rhyme. When the children can recite to 6 confidently (this may take many weeks) develop the activity by asking them to count their sticks in front of them, assessing their one-to-one correspondence with just one number word for each time they point to or pick up a stick. When most are confident with that, develop the activity with the children holding the sticks in their hand (so instead of being a long line, all the sticks are together in a small bundle). Add on to the rhyme:

   Make a bundle, make it small
   I can count them, count them all.

- ◆ Then count again and establish that there are still 6.

◆ Group activities

Focus group

Assess reciting and one-to-one correspondence. Use number cards (or Unifix number indicators) and first ask them to lay them in order and then count along the line. Then ask each child to lay out a corresponding number of objects next to each card, (or make towers of Unifix). Take each child as far as they can go both in reciting number names and counting objects. You can then set individual targets, for example with a child who can count to 5, set a target of learning to recite to 10 by the end of term.

6
©Hopscotch Educational Publishing

developing
**Numeracy
Skills**

Numeracy
Reception/P1

Counting to 10

 Teacher independent groups

✦ **Group 1:** Use play dough to make birthday cakes/ cherry buns/bugs (on boards or oven trays) and use sticks/buttons to make candles/cherries/spots. Say *"Choose number cards to go with the number of candles on your cakes."* Provide old birthday cards with numbers on them. (See also Chapter 5.)

✦ **Group 2:** Using stamper pens, these children stamp a number all of one shape (such as seven stars) and write that number next to their set to take to the plenary session. Provide other equipment with numbers on, such as coins or number puzzles.

✦ **Group 3:** These children count out objects onto trays labelled with the numbers 4 to 10, or count as far as they can with anything they want to.

✦ *Plenary session*

✦ Ask the children to count out their objects: *"How many candles on this cake Abdul? Let's count them all together. You point as we count."* Assess whether they are reciting the number names in order and, if they are, whether they are counting with one number word for each number. More experienced children could show how far they can count. Note how far individuals can recite numbers.

LESSON TWO — IS IT STILL THE SAME?

✦ *Assessment focus*

✦ Can children understand that the number remains the same however the objects are grouped?

✦ *Resources*

✦ paper bugs and cubes or buttons for spots

✦ *Oral work and mental calculation*

✦ Recite to 4, 5 or above using fingers for counting.
✦ Write the numbers on the board and ask the children to point with their finger to follow how you are forming numbers.

✦ *Starting point: Whole class*

✦ Each child needs 3 cubes or buttons. Sit in a circle and lead them in rearranging their buttons, for example *"2 over here and 1 right over there, do we still have 3?"* The children may want to count each time and that is fine at the start, but encourage them to think about whether any buttons have gone – so there must still be 3. For some children that will take more practice. They are likely to say there are more when the buttons are in a long line. Agree that the line is longer, but match them to 3 fingers and establish that there are still 3 buttons. Move them close together – there are still 3. You could use paper bugs of different shapes and sizes as on activity sheets: *"Two spots on this side, how many on that side?"* Or use Activity sheet 2. *"So we arranged them in a different way, but there are still 3 buttons."*

Counting to 10

♦ Group activities

Focus group

Use Activity sheet 2 or a different paper outline of a bug for each child. Repeat the starter activity with a different number of buttons, assessing children's abilities and their use of language. such as *"There is still the same number"* and *"I don't need to count them because there must still be four"*.

 Teacher independent groups

Use the photocopiable activity sheets.

✦ **Activity sheet 1:** This activity involves children in experiencing the same number of dots in different shapes and arrangements. They should draw lines to match the bugs that have the same number of spots. The first line is drawn for them and two others are dotted for them to draw over. Encourage them to match the dots on one bug to buttons or cubes, then move those buttons to another bug and talk about what happens.

✦ **Activity sheet 2:** Using four cubes, the children draw around each cube. Ask *"Do you have a different number of spots here or is it the same number?"*

✦ **Activity sheet 3:** Select a number for the lower part of the sheet or let the children choose one. You can make sheets with no numbers by photocopying the lower part of the sheet twice and sticking them together. You or the child choose numbers.

Plenary session

✦ Question the children about their drawings: *"But that is a long line of dots, are you sure there are the same number as this bunch of dots? How do you know?"* (Look for the children to count and say it is the same number.) *"Does that look more than that? Is it the same number of dots/cubes?"* Repeat the whole-class starter with a different number of cubes.

♦ Further activities

✦ Recite numbers in order, such as 'One, two, three, four, five, once I caught a fish alive'.
✦ Keep reciting to 6 then 10 until all children are confident.
✦ Use words for quantity by doing the starter in Lesson Two but this time give children one more cube so that you can say that now it isn't the same number, it is one more.
✦ Play track number games, such as Ludo and Snakes and Ladders.
✦ Count things that cannot be moved.
✦ Count things that cannot be touched.

♦ Extension

✦ Let the children explore arrangements of spots with a larger number, such as 10, to find as many different arrangements as they can make with their number and draw some of them.

Support

✦ Children who need more practice at conservation of number should do plenty of counting activities with real objects, such as putting the right number of sorting toys in a pot to match the number card. Try to get every child reciting to 10 as soon as possible.

✦ **Match the spots** ✦

✦ Match the bugs with the same number of spots.

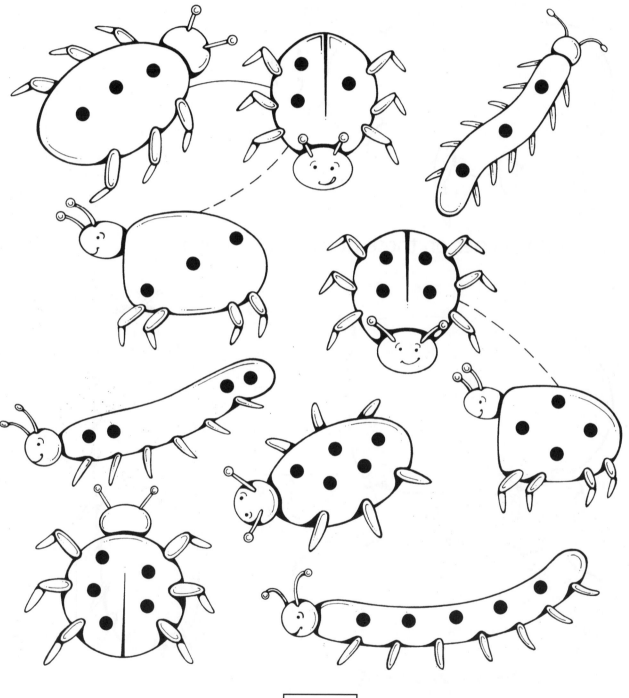

 Draw more bugs with ⬚ spots.

✦ How many? ✦

✦ Use 4 cubes. Put your cubes on this bug.

How many?

Now put the cubes on these bugs. Write how many.

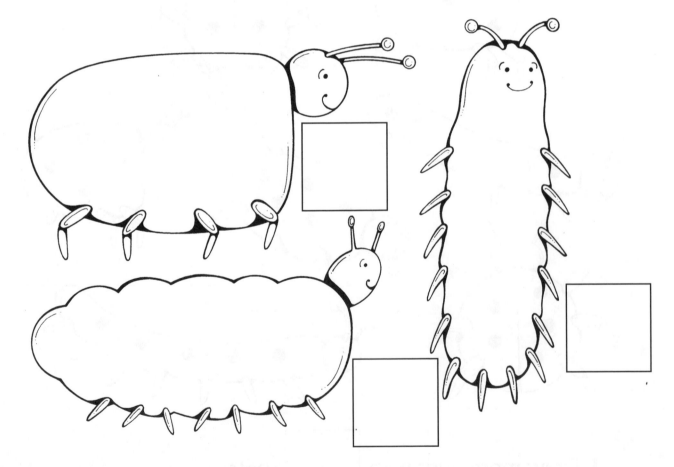

 Draw some bugs with 1 more cube.

developing
Numeracy Skills

✦ Match the spots ✦

✦ Make each bug have 4 spots. Make a different pattern each time.

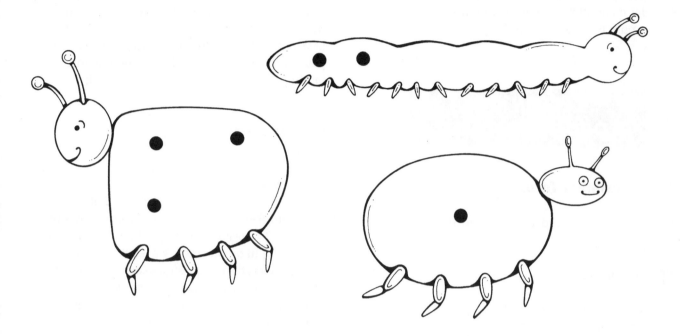

✦ Choose a number. Make each bug have the same number. Make different patterns.

Ordering and comparing

 ### Overall learning objectives

✦ Learn the vocabulary of comparing and ordering.
✦ Order a complete sequence of numbers.
✦ Compare two numbers and say which is more or less.

LESSON ONE ORDERING TO 10

 ### Assessment focus

✦ Can the children order numbers to 10?

 ### Resources

✦ a large floor number line
✦ socks and washing line
✦ number cards
✦ outline of bugmobile (see activity sheets)
✦ buttons
✦ toy cars and trucks

 ### Oral work and mental calculation

Numbers to 10

✦ Say some number rhymes with numbers in order, such as 'One, two, three, four, five. Once I caught a fish alive.' Hang some socks on a washing line. Do finger counting to 10 and match words to large digit cards or to the sock washing line. Say *"This sock has a 4 on it. Hold up that many fingers. What is this next number? Hold up that many fingers."*

 ### Starting point: Whole class

✦ Use a large floor number line so that children who need it can repeat reciting numbers, making one step for each number word. Move on to ordering cards on the carpet. Tell the children to

shut their eyes while you secretly turn one card over or move one or more out of position. Can they put the numbers back in order? Leave this on display ready for group tasks. Next, count the wheels on toy cars to introduce the group tasks. (Ask particular children to the front to count so you can assess counting skills.) Demonstrate joining a dot-to-dot picture on the board.

  ### Group activities

 Focus group

Have an outline of a 'bugmobile' (see Activity sheet 2) but with no wheels. Using buttons for wheels, ask one child to put 2 wheels on the bugmobile, then ask the next child to put on one more wheel. Repeat this with several numbers asking questions such as *"Is 3 more or less than 4?"* and *"What number is one more than 5?"* Then observe each child ordering number cards from 1 to 10 (include zero for some) or putting out the right number of cubes on each number card 1 to 10.

Teacher independent groups

Use the photocopiable activity sheets.

✦ **Activity sheet 1:** The children should first put the number cards to 10 in order, then do the dot-to-dot activity. They should then draw the correct number of wheels for each bugmobile according to the number that is written on them.

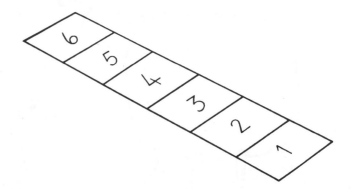

Ordering and comparing

✦ **Activity sheet 2:** The children should cut out the bugmobiles then put them in order starting with one wheel. On a separate sheet they should draw the missing bugmobiles (2 and 8). Stick them all on to a long bit of paper to make a number line.

✦ **Activity sheet 3:** This activity is for children who can draw the correct number of wheels for each bugmobile in order from 1 to 10.

✦ Plenary session

✦ Together say the numbers in order to 10. Look at the number lines made and count along them. Ask a child from each group to share with the class their activity sheet. Count together the number of wheels on the bugmobiles.

LESSON TWO
WHICH IS MORE?

✦ Assessment focus

✦ Can children compare two numbers and say which is more?

✦ Resources

✦ a washing line and pegs
✦ several pairs of socks
✦ blank paper socks
✦ paper or card socks with numbers written on
✦ pairs of items, such as a brush and comb
✦ items for counting
✦ pots

✦ Oral work and mental calculation

Counting more/fewer

✦ Count some socks (at least to 6) and sort them into pairs. Lay them on the carpet and ask children to come out in turns to pick up a different number of socks. *"Jack come and count out 3 socks. Jean come and count out 4. Who has the most?"* Hang some socks on the washing line. Count out another set of socks, either more or fewer, and hang them in a different place on the line. Ask *"Are there more on that side of the line, or*

more over here? So 6 is more than 4." Put paper socks on the line numbered in order to about 6, for children to continue using at group time.

✦ Starting point: Whole class

✦ Play a circle game: each child copies how many fingers you hold up. Hold up 3 and say *"I'm holding up 3 fingers."* They must copy. Count them slowly together, pointing to each finger in turn, emphasising one number name for each finger. When children can do this, ask them to hold up more fingers than you do. They can choose how many more. Say *"How many are you holding up Saphie? Yasmeen, is 4 more than 1?"* and so on until they are confident. Then play around the circle – each child in turn holds up a few fingers and says to the child next to them, *"I'm holding up 4 fingers. You hold up more."* That child holds up more, they are counted and you help with a number sentence: *"5 is more than 4."* Vary the game with holding up fewer fingers.

Ordering and comparing

◆ Group activities

Focus group

◆ Assess children's language of number and counting skills, such as *"Tell me a number that is more than 2."*; *"Can you put these number cards/socks in order?"*; *"How many in this pile? Is that more or fewer than 4?"*; *"Give me one fewer than 3."*; *"Hide some of these teddies. Do we now have more or fewer teddies?"*

Teacher independent groups

NOTE At this age the children will not be able to work independently on comparing numbers. Therefore these are play activities which will help them to consolidate understanding of numbers.

◆ **Group 1:** provide pairs of socks for children to match and count. If some are still just counting to 2 provide other pairs, such as a brush and comb, toothbrush and toothpaste. (If appropriate let the children pretend to wash the socks and hang them on the line to count at review time.)

◆ **Group 2:** provide pens, paper, number cards and items to count, pots to count into. The children should count and draw the number of items they have counted. You could give individuals specific numbers to count (about 3 for each child).

◆ **Group 3:** give these children 'blank' paper socks and ask them to add more numbers to the washing line, in order, making the numbers large and clear. (Provide ready made paper numbers if you want.) They need to work co-operatively so that they don't end up with more than one sock for each number.

◆ Plenary session

◆ *"Let's count how many socks on Peter's line. Has Jubeen got more socks?"*
◆ *"Is 2 more or less than 1?"*
◆ *"Which of your pots had the fewest cubes?"*
◆ *"Help me to put these numbered socks in order on the washing line. Shut your eyes and I will move two out of order, then you tell me which they are."*
◆ *"What is 1 more than 2?"*
◆ *"Which number comes just after 3?"*
◆ *"What is 2 less than 5?"*

◆ Further activities

◆ Order numbers to 10 and 20. Lay them on the carpet in different arrangements. Ask the children to shut their eyes. Swap two cards and ask them which you moved.
◆ Put selected numbers in order, such as 4, 7, 2 and 1.
◆ Use ordinal numbers: 1st, 2nd and so on, such as when getting ready for PE.
◆ Say a number lying between two others using the floor number line. For example, *"Liam stand on 5 and Diane stand on 2. Tell me a number than is between 5 and 2."*

◆ Extension

◆ Let the children order numbers above 100.

◆ Support

◆ Use number cards in order and match them to that many Unifix. Keep stressing *"4 is one more than 3."* *"6 comes after 5 because it is one more than 5."*
◆ Ask the children the numbers on the paper socks on the washing line each day. Sometimes make the socks out of order and ask children to put them back in order.
◆ Make sand numbers for those still needing help with forming numbers. Paint over the numbers with white glue and sprinkle with sand. Leave to dry, cut out, stick onto card with a coloured band at the bottom that you teach the child to hold, so they hold it the right way up, then mark the starting point for each number with a bold dot.

◆ **Bugmobiles** ◆

◆ Join the dots.

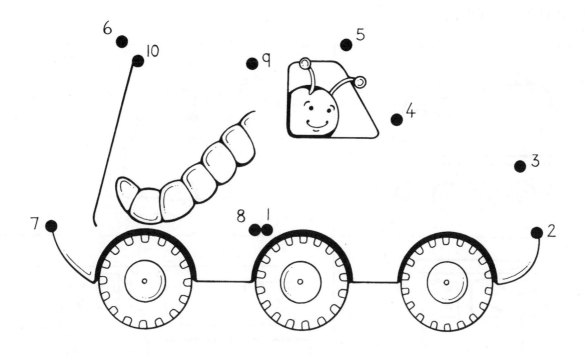

◆ Draw the right number of wheels on each bugmobile.

 Now draw a bugmobile with 5 wheels.

◆ **Bugmobiles** ◆

✦ Cut out these bugmobiles. Two are missing. Draw them
  and put them all in order to make a line of bugmobiles
  with wheels from 1 to 10.

developing
Numeracy
Skills

Photocopiable

©Hopscotch Educational Publishing

✦ **Bugmobiles** ✦

✦ Draw wheels on these bugmobiles, starting with
1 wheel on the first then 1 more each time until
the last one has 10 wheels.

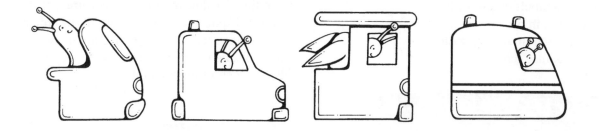

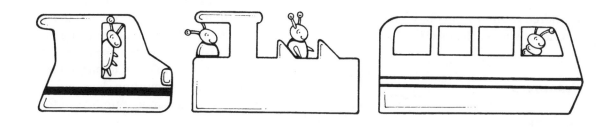

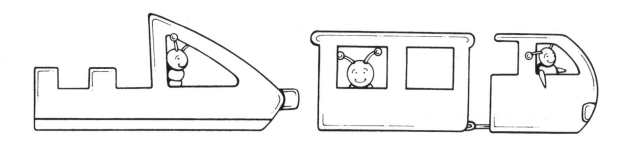

developing
Numeracy
Skills

Recording

 Overall learning objectives

✦ Read numbers (and number names).
✦ Order numbers to 10 and above.
✦ Tally one mark for each object and begin to understand symbols and recording.
✦ Recite numbers in order.
✦ Count on/back from a given number.
✦ Begin to recognise zero.

LESSON ONE TALLYING

 Assessment focus

✦ Can children count a set of objects reliably and make one tally for each object?

 Resources

✦ a large paper bug with about 40 or 50 spots
✦ a large spotty dice
✦ number cards
✦ lots of identical yoghurt pots
✦ cubes/buttons
✦ teddies and a toy tea set
✦ butterbeans coloured blue on one side

 Oral work and mental calculation

Matching fingers to number cards

✦ Say a number rhyme and use fingers to count and match to related number cards. Quickly hold up different numbers of fingers and ask the children to call out the number. Ask individual children out to the front of the class to hold up fingers and other children find the related number card. Develop number sentences using a wide range of mathematical language, for example *"We started with 5 ducks, now we only have 3. Is that more than 5 or fewer than 5?"*

 Starting point: Whole class

✦ Play 'spotty bug' using the large outline drawing of a bug. In two teams, each using a different colour, the children take turns to throw the dice, count the dice dots then mark the corresponding number of spots on the bug, with all the children counting together as these marks are made. Check for one to one correspondence, one mark or tally for each number count.

 Group activities

 Focus group

Give each child a handful of cubes or buttons, just over the number they can count to independently. Show them how to make one tally for each item. They will need to move the objects as they count them, or put them in a pot to prevent counting items twice. Assess counting skills and try to take each child on a few more numbers in their counting.

Teacher independent groups

NOTE At this age not all the children will be able to do tallying activities on their own, so these activities are play activities related to basic counting skills.

✦ Group 1: Give each child three or more teddies and ask them to give each teddy one plate, one bowl, one cup, one spoon and so on.

Recording

♦ **Group 2:** This group should do the same activity as Group 1 but then draw a picture to show the teddy with the objects, using simple shapes for each item, such as a circle for a plate. This is one approach to tallying.

♦ **Group 3:** Provide ten butter beans coloured blue on one side. In turn, the children throw the beans and count the number that land blue side up, then on a sheet of paper, make a tally mark for each one.

LESSON TWO USING SYMBOLS

♦ Assessment focus

♦ Can the children count with one number word for each step or item and begin to see the meaning of symbols and record them?

♦ Resources

♦ counters and dice
♦ yoghurt pots
♦ paper
♦ number cards and a number line

♦ Oral work and mental calculation

Chanting numbers

♦ Count around the circle to a number suitable for your children (everyone chanting the numbers together), then start from 1 again. (Later in the term try to go all round the circle chanting up to as far as they can go.) *"Now let's start from 3 and see if we can count up to 7. Now let's go back again to 3."* (Keep chanting all together until they are very confident and some can do it on their own.)

♦ Plenary session

♦ Look at the groupings the children in Group 1 have made. Is there one of each item for each teddy? Look at the pictures drawn by Group 2. As a class count together the numbers of teddies and objects. The focus group children can demonstrate their tallying. Repeat the focus group activity all together as a class.

♦ Starting point: Whole class

♦ Using a large floor number track, ask who can see the numbers. (If most children are not able to work with numbers yet, mark them with objects such as a ball and a pencil so that you can say, *"How many steps from the pencil to the ball?"*) The children take turns to step along the track starting from 0. Take care to teach them that they count 1 for each step taken and mustn't count as 1 the space they are standing on. *"Patrick, stand on the symbol for zero. Take one step. Which number are you on now? Look at the symbol for 1 and draw it in the air. Now take two steps. Which number do you land on? Draw it in the air."* You could draw these numbers on the board.

♦ Group activities

 Focus group

Give each child two identical yoghurt pots. They put 1 counter in one pot and 2 counters in the other. They then cover their pots with a piece of paper and muddle them up. They have to guess which one is which. Then take the paper lids off the pots and ask them to put something on the paper lid that will let them know which pot is which. So, they must find a symbol for 1 and 2. Replace the lids, muddle the pots up and ask them one at a time to look at their lids and tell you which pot has 1 counter. Explain that we use symbols to help us to know how many. Repeat this with four identical pots and the numbers 0–3 or 1–4.

Recording

Teacher independent groups

Use the photocopiable activity sheets.

✦ **Activity sheet 1:** The children need a 1–6 dice for each pair and cards 1–6 (these can have dots as well if that is needed). They take turns to throw the dice and match them to the number of bugs and number card, writing the matching number (or drawing dots or making tallies) in the space. When they have thrown all the numbers, they can cut out each rectangle and stick them in order to make a bug number line for their desk or to take home.

✦ **Activity sheet 2:** First the children should carefully write the numbers 0 to 9, tracing over the dots. Then, they should write in the missing numbers on the bugmobiles and foot print number lines.

✦ **Activity sheet 3:** The children need to be able to see a number line to 20. They then write in the missing numbers on each of the number lines.

✦ *Plenary session*

✦ Show some of the symbols that the focus group made. *"So when Sophie saw this symbol, she knew there were 2 in that pot."*
✦ Count the bugs on Activity sheet 1 and ask one child to write on the board the related dots, another the tallies and a third the numbers. Recite 1 to 6 in order.
✦ Ask children who have done Activity sheets 2 and 3 to show their work.
✦ Together count from 0 to 20, pointing to the symbols on the number as you do so.

✦ *Further activities*

✦ Find more symbols, for example the + and = on the calculator.
✦ On the maths table provide each child with a copy of Generic sheet 1 on page 90 together with some butter beans which have been coloured blue on one side. The children have to throw 10 beans and count the number that land blue side up. They write that number in the appropriate column, being careful to record the number correctly. If they have already thrown that number three times they can't fill in a box. The winner is the player who has the most number of lines with three numbers filled in. The game can continue at another time until each player has filled in all their numbers.

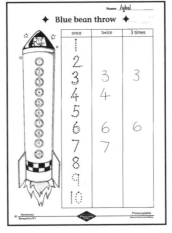

◆ *Extension*

✦ Extend the number line to 30 and above.
✦ Start at 3 and count to 13, then count back again. Ask the children to tell you a number that comes between 3 and 13. Ask someone to come and write it on the board. Do the others agree? Are there more possibilities?

✦ *Support*

✦ Keep giving experience in counting one number word for each item or step on the number line. Make sure all children can recite to 10 and do this as they take 10 steps along the number line. Help them to recognise the symbols for these numbers.
✦ Extend the bug number line made with Activity sheet 1 up to at least 10 and use it for counting out the right number of cubes and putting these on the appropriate number.

◆ How many? ◆

You need: a dice and some number cards.

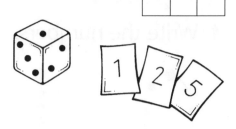

◆ Throw the dice. Use dots, tallies or
   symbols to write the numbers.

Numeracy
Reception/P1

developing
Numeracy Skills

Photocopiable
©Hopscotch Educational Publishing

21

Name _____

◆ Write the numbers ◆

◆ Write the numbers.

     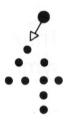

◆ Write the missing numbers.

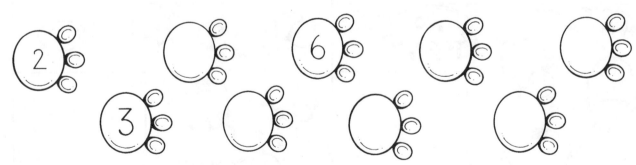

| 0 | 1 | 2 | 3 | 4 | 5 | 6 | 7 | 8 | 9 | 10 |

developing **Numeracy Skills**

Name _____

✦ **Missing numbers** ✦

✦ Write the missing numbers in the number lines.

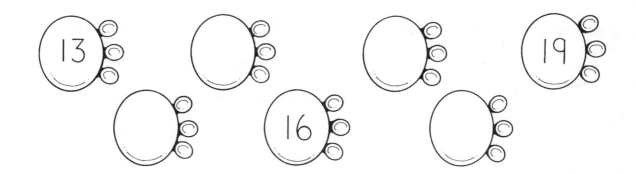

Counting and estimating

 ◆ **Overall learning objectives**

◆ Count reliably to 20 and above.
◆ Begin to write and name numbers above 10 and 20.
◆ Estimate a number in the range that can be counted reliably, then check by counting.

LESSON ONE COUNTING BEYOND 10

◆ **Assessment focus**

◆ Can the children recite to 20 or beyond?

◆ **Resources**

◆ 100 square or number line to 100 on display
◆ dice/spinner
◆ counters
◆ number cards

◆ **Oral work and mental calculation**

Chanting numbers beyond 20

◆ Together as a class, chant the numbers up to and beyond 20. Then ask questions such as *"What number follows 15?"* and *"What number comes before 20?"*

 ◆ **Starting point: Whole class**

◆ Say *"On my imaginary number line, I am zero, and the wall is 10. So 1 is here and 2 is there. Where will we put 5?"*
◆ *"Now let's make Jack zero and send Abdul over there to be 20. Where 10 will be? Where will 15 be?"*
◆ Show the numbers on a 100 square and/or on a number line. Count along them. Ask individual children to point to specific numbers.

 ◆ **Group activities**

 Focus group

Give the children some number cards according to their experience. They should count out that many objects (things that might be seen around the room). Check that only one number name is given to each object. Assess other counting skills. For example, rearrange their objects and ask them how many there are now. Ask individuals to count items that can't be touched or moved, such as the window panes.

 Teacher independent groups

Use the photocopiable activity sheets.

◆ **Activity sheet 1:** This is a cycling dragon board game, using a 1–6 dice or a spinner. The children work in pairs, first writing the missing numbers on the dragon, then taking turns to throw the dice and move their counter from the head that many steps. The first to reach the tail is the winner but they must throw the right number to finish. This sheet only goes to 20.

◆ **Activity sheet 2:** Again the children must write the missing numbers, then use dice and counters to race to the end.

◆ **Activity sheet 3:** Again the children must write the missing numbers, then use dice and counters to race to the end of the number track. (See Further activities on page 26 for other ways of using this sheet.)

◆ **Plenary session**

◆ Let the groups tell the class about the games they played and who won. Ask the children to count in 1s to 40, then to 100. Show the numbers on a large 100 square or number line.

Counting and estimating

 Assessment focus

+ Can the children make reasonable estimates and then check by counting?

 Resources

+ a large 100 square
+ prepared cards made with stamper pens or stickers with between 1 and 15 stars or shapes
+ two clear jars the same size
+ 'sweets' large and small
+ further jars filled with small sweets or buttons
+ green paper for 'gardens'
+ cubes, spinner, number line
+ children's stamp pads or paint, stamper pens

 Oral work and mental calculation

Larger numbers

+ Help the children to count together as far as they can go. Point to the numbers on a 100 square and demonstrate the pattern in the sounds of the numbers once we get beyond 19 (24, 34, 44, 54 and so on).
+ Demonstrate large numbers by getting children to stand up and hold up fingers, for example 20 fingers with 2 children, or 4 children holding up 5 fingers each. Count all the children in the class and find the number on the 100 square.

 Starting point: Whole class

+ Ask one child to stand on a number on a number line and the others to hold up fingers to show how many that number is. Then establish that beyond 10 the number is too big for just one person to hold up fingers – but we can use toes as well!

+ Move to the carpet and show two jars of 'sweets', about 5 large sweets in one jar and about 10 smaller ones in the other. Ask the children to estimate how many, then let some come to the front to count them. Show another jar with many small sweets and ask for estimates. Establish that it would take a long time to count them and explain that the groups will do that later.
+ Use estimation cards such as those below. Make them with just a few more or less than 10 (8, 9, 11 and 12), using stickers or stamper pens. Make some with large stickers and some with smaller ones and different arrangements. Ask *"Is the number of shapes on this card about 3 or about 10?"* Emphasise that estimating is very important and that you aren't asking them to count just yet, just to say which number they think it might be nearest to. Then count them together. By giving choices of numbers we help children to see that they do not need to count at first.

Estimation cards

 Group activities

 Focus group

Start with two jars, one with small objects and one with larger ones and ask for estimates so you can assess individuals. Review counting skills. Assess if children can take a handful of about ten. Play 'bugs in the garden' – have a large clear number line and lots of 'bugs' (cubes) and a 'garden'. Each child takes some bugs to play in their garden (they choose the number). Ask them to choose somewhere between 'about' 3 and 7 bugs (or to suit their experience). Then pick a card or spin a spinner and mark that number on the number line and see who thinks they have the number of bugs closest to that number.

Counting and estimating

Ask them to guess how many jumps they need to make to get to the spinner number, for example *"If Sam chose 5 bugs, estimate how many more would he need to have 11."*

 Teacher independent groups

✦ **Group 1:** Working in pairs, ask the children to take it in turns to print a number of shapes (adjust the size of paper and printing shape for the numbers individuals can use), not counting but estimating. The partner then counts them to see how close they were.

✦ **Group 2:** Give out 'sweets' in a jar (a number that will be fairly demanding for the children to count) to each pair. One child takes small handful out and places it on the table. The other child estimates how many and they record the estimate. They then count. If they are close they can put a smiley face by their estimate.

✦ **Group 3:** One at a time around the table, this group takes two enormous handfuls (or more) of cubes. Each person in the group guesses how many and writes down their estimate. The cubes are then quietly counted by joining them into cube trains of 10. They then secretly find the number on the big 100 square and write it down.

 Plenary session

✦ Demonstrate 'bugs in the garden' and ask who is nearest, who chose more than someone else. *"How many bugs did Anna have? Did Brian have more or fewer?"*

✦ Hold up some of the prints, ask for estimates, then count and write clear numbers for a display. Establish that you can only get a few large prints on some pages but you can get lots of tiny prints. You can display a group of prints of 'about 10'.

✦ Review estimates and counting of sweets, counting 10-cube trains (10, 20, 30 and so on).

✦ ***Further activities***

✦ Repeat Lesson Two using the cards with around 20 stickers and around 100 stickers.

✦ Repeat with different sweets/biscuits/cubes and different sizes of jars.

✦ Help the children to chant in hundreds (100, 200, 300 and so on) and later with thousands (at this stage they are just hearing the pattern).

✦ Activity sheet 1 can be used for a variety of track games, such as throw two dice, add the numbers and move on that many.

✦ Activity sheet 2 can be used for track games. The children throw a 1–6 dice and spin a spinner that has 'add 1' and 'add 2'. They do the sum and move that many spaces.

✦ Activity sheet 3 can be used to create a number line that goes along a wall. Generic sheet 2 (page 91) fits on to this sheet at both ends.

✦ ***Extension***

✦ Collect 100 of something, such as buttons. Put 10 in each pot. How many pots?

✦ ***Support***

✦ Do more estimation of 'sweets' in jars and check by counting.

26
©Hopscotch Educational Publishing

developing
Numeracy
Skills

Numeracy
Reception/P1

✦ Dragon game ✦

✦ Write in the missing numbers. Then play with a partner.
  Use a dice or spinner. See who can reach the end first.

developing Numeracy Skills
©Hopscotch Educational Publishing

◆ Caterpillar game ◆

◆ Write in the missing numbers. Then play with a partner.
  Use a dice or spinner. See who can reach the end first.

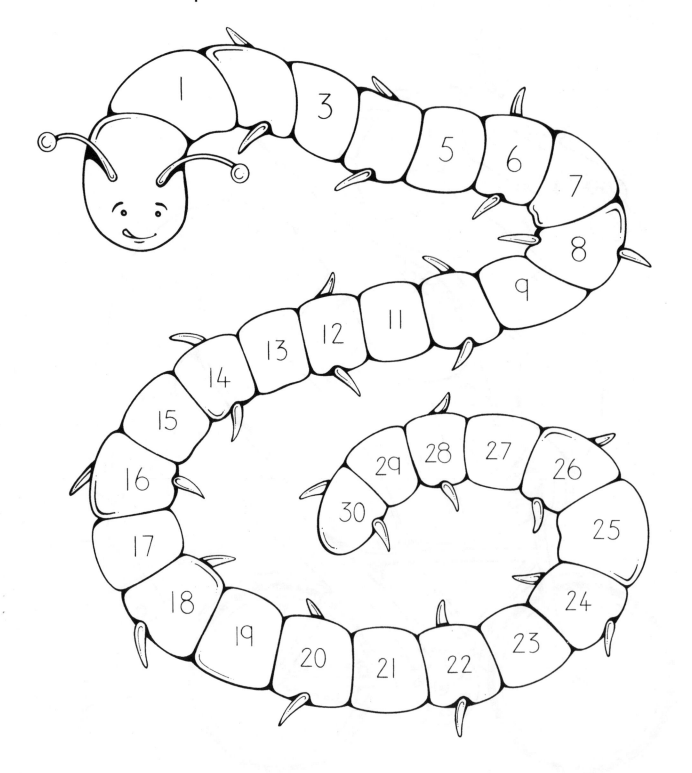

◆ Number track ◆

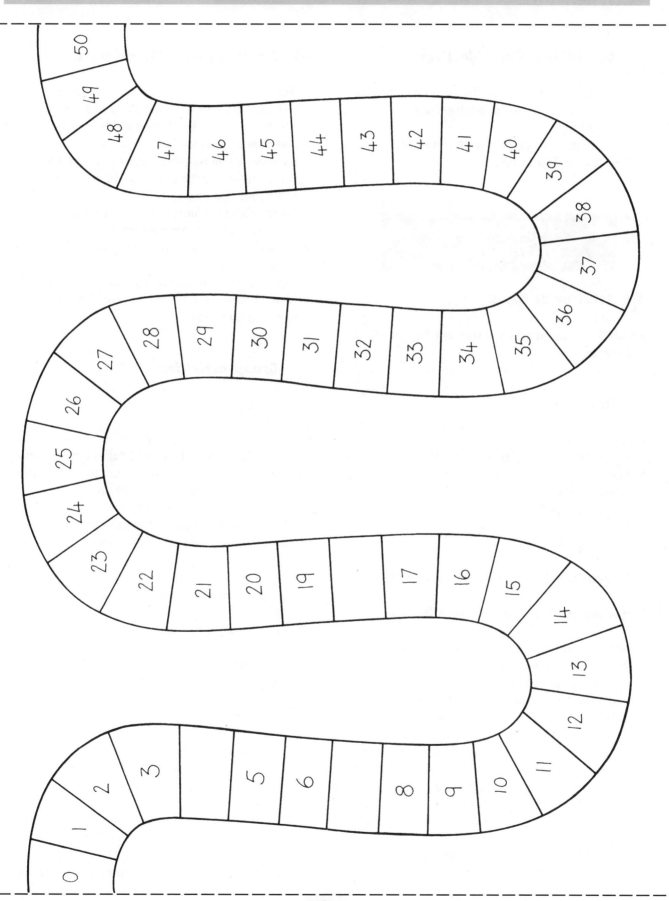

©Hopscotch Educational Publishing

developing
Numeracy
Skills

Using a number line

◆ Overall learning objectives

- ✦ In practical activities and discussion begin to use the language involved in addition and subtraction.
- ✦ Find one more or one less than a number.
- ✦ Counting in 2s and 10s.

**LESSON ONE
JUMPING ONE**

◆ Assessment focus

- ✦ Can the children add and subtract 1 to and from low numbers?

◆ Resources

- ✦ number cards
- ✦ a large floor number line and small number lines
- ✦ dice
- ✦ cubes, plastic teddies or superbugs

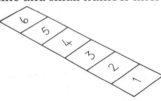

◆ Oral work and mental calculation

Counting to 10/12/20 and counting back

- ✦ Play '10 jump up'. Sit the children in a circle and count around the circle. The child who is 10 has to jump up quickly as everyone says "10". Start from 1 again. Go on until ten children are standing up. (This game works well in a space where noise doesn't matter!) Change the game to '12/20 jump up' but stop at an agreed number of children standing up.
- ✦ Do finger counting, asking *"What is one more than that number?"* Say a counting back in ones rhyme, such as 'Five little ducks went swimming one day' and show related number cards. Say *"Tom, come and find the card that shows a three. Which card is one less/more?"*

◆ Starting point: Whole class

- ✦ Stand around the large floor number line and revise reciting from 1 to 10. *"Josie, stand on 4 then jump one. Where do you land? So we say that if you start on 4 and jump one, you land on 5. 4 and 1 more makes 5. Everyone do that with their fingers."* (At some stage before the end of the year you will need explicitly to talk about zero and your 'zero space' at the end of the number line. Start a child on this space. Say *"Where will you get to if you jump on one space?"*)
- ✦ Show them how to draw a jump on a number line (as on Activity sheet 2). Let confident children come out to demonstrate this on the board.
- ✦ Now (or in a later lesson) you could move on to jumping back one.

◆ Group activities

Focus group

Either use Activity sheet 2 or some number lines on the table with plastic teddies or cubes jumping along the line to assess each child's ability to understand and use the related vocabulary of adding/ subtracting 1. Say *"4, jump 1 makes 5, jump back 1 and you get back to 4 again."* You might be able to use numbers over 10 with some children.

Teacher independent groups

Use the photocopiable activity sheets.

- ✦ **Activity sheet 1:** These children will need number lines and a plastic superbug (or cube) to jump. They (or you) choose numbers for the bottom part of the sheet.

- ✦ **Activity sheet 2:** The children should draw in the third jump. Let them use plastic teddies/superbugs to make the jumps.

- ✦ **Activity sheet 3:** You can write suitable numbers on the sheet or let the children take a card from a pack of cards numbered from 3 to 10. At first they should take one jump each time,

Using a number line

then throw a dice for the number of jumps. There is space in the 'jump' column for 'jump backs'.

Plenary session

✦ Go over the numbers the children have used on their sheets, encouraging a wide range of

language. *"So you are saying that one more than 9 is 10. Is he right?"*

✦ Play a game where one child stands out at the front and shows a number of fingers. The others count them and add/subtract 1. Change the game so that a child holds up a number card. Then try it with no cards and no fingers. Say *"Think of 3 in your mind and add/take away 1."*

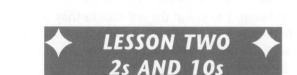

LESSON TWO
2s AND 10s

Assessment focus

✦ Can the children count in 2s at least to 10?

Resources

✦ a Noah's ark
✦ a number line
✦ 100 square
✦ a box of green cubes

Oral work and mental calculation

Counting in 2s

✦ Teach a simple counting in 2s rhyme.
> *Two, four,*
> *Six, eight, ten,*
> *Frogs are hopping through the fen.*
> *Two, four,*
> *Six, eight, ten,*
> *Counting on and back again.*

(You need to say the 'Two, four' fairly slowly.)

✦ Establish that counting 'on' means going up towards 10.

✦ Lay out number cards 2, 4, 6, 8 and 10. Tell the children to close their eyes. You then move a couple of cards out of place and ask one child to

put them back in order. Ask confident children to chant in 2s to 10 in pairs. Leave actually counting back again until they are confident and even then, go very slowly.

Starting point: Whole class

✦ Count fingers in 2s. Say *"Two and two more makes 4 and another 2 makes 6."* Show them the jumps on the number line.

✦ Use a handful of cubes to demonstrate how it can be quicker to count lots of things if we put them in groups of 2 (or 10), then we can check easily.

Group activities

Focus group

Set up a counting in 2s task that goes beyond 10, such as seats in a bus or aeroplane. Let the children put out chairs, *"2 here and 2 there. Now let's count how many passengers we have space for."* Use the number line to count in 2s, jumping along it with your finger. Ask some of the children to make finger jumps along the line. Assess familiarity with numbers up to and beyond 10.

Using a number line

Teacher independent groups

✦ **Group 1:** Set up a Noah's ark (you could use a cardboard box and Plasticine animals) in the place where you will have the plenary session. (This can also make an interactive display.) Using 2 or 3 pairs of animals and with even number cards from 2 to 10, the children have to put the animals in the ark in 2s and order the number cards. They should have access to a number line as they do this (although at this age they will probably just play.)

✦ **Group 2:** This group can play simple games where they can score in 2s and keep the total with cubes. For example, they throw bean bags on to a target and score 2 for each successful throw. Again they should refer to the number line as they do this.

✦ **Group 3:** Provide a box containing all the same thing, such as green cubes to represent frogs. The children have to count out all the 'frogs' in the box and then count them in 2s. Again they should be referring to the number line. Some children will be able to count in 10s, so you could provide a bigger box full of cubes and ask them to put them in piles of 10.

Plenary session

✦ Children from the focus group should explain what they have been doing and say how many passengers there were chairs for. Ask children from Group 1 to count the animals as they go into the ark in pairs. Group 3 could tell the class how many frogs they found in the box, then count them in 2s out loud.

✦ Say *"Someone come and show me the card that says 10. What comes after 10 when we count in 2s? Can you find it on the number line?"*

✦ Show the children the pattern of the 2s on the 100 square. Count in 2s together as far as you can go. Repeat this several times in the next few weeks so that all can recite at least to 10.

Further activities

✦ Have a spinner with '1 more' and '1 less' and repeat the floor number line starter in Lesson One, with a child spinning the spinner to decide if they are to count back or on. Use a wide range of vocabulary, such as *"7 is 1 less than 8"* and *"the number that is 1 more than 6 is 7"*. Extend numbers above 10 and 20 on a 100 square to show the pattern.

✦ Count in 10s by rote and by using an activity like counting the 'frogs' in Lesson 2, Group 3.

✦ Using Generic sheet 4 (page 93), in pairs the children could throw a dice, put out that many cubes, then add 1 and have to tell their partner what they did. *"I threw a 3 and 1 more makes 4 so I am putting 4 cubes on my side."* The winner is first to cover their side of the sheet. (Either the teacher or the children could write the numbers 1 to 5 at the bottom of the sheet.)

Extension

✦ Let the children explore numbers on the 100 square. For example, give them selected number cards, such as 23, 17, 31, 67 and ask them to find the number that is one more, circle it on the 100 square and then write it on the board. *"What is 1 more than 100? How do you write that number?"*

Support

✦ Keep doing finger counting at mental maths time. Say *"Look, Zac is holding up 6 fingers. What is 1 more than 6?"*

Name _____

◆ Jump 1 ◆

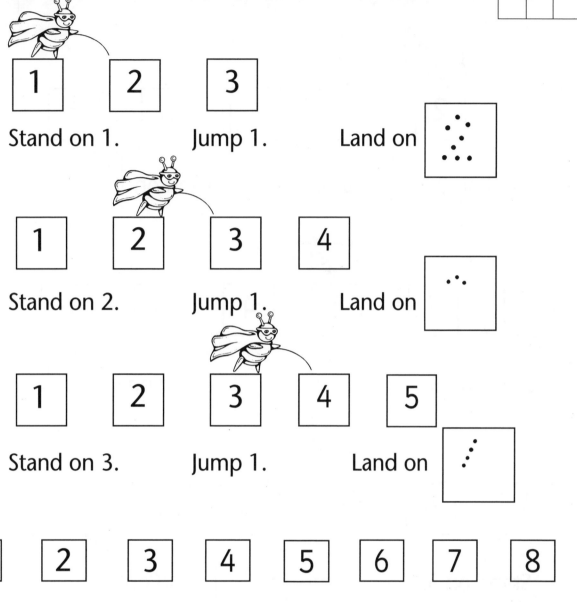

| 1 | 2 | 3 |

Stand on 1.   Jump 1.   Land on

| 1 | 2 | 3 | 4 |

Stand on 2.   Jump 1.   Land on

| 1 | 2 | 3 | 4 | 5 |

Stand on 3.   Jump 1.   Land on

| 1 | 2 | 3 | 4 | 5 | 6 | 7 | 8 |

Stand on ☐   Jump ☐   Land on ☐

Stand on ☐   Jump ☐   Land on ☐

📖 Write the numbers from 1 to 10.

developing **Numeracy Skills**

◆ Where do you land? ◆

1	2	3	4	5	6

Stand on 2.   Jump 1.   Land on [ ]

1	2	3	4	5	6

Stand on 3.   Jump 1.   Land on [ ]

3	4	5	6	7	8

Stand on 5.   Jump [ ]   Land on [ ]

Do some more superbug jumps.
Record them in your own way.

1	2	3	4	5	6	7	8

Numeracy
Reception/P1

developing
**Numeracy
Skills**

Photocopiable

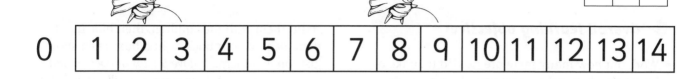

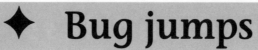 **Bug jumps** ✦

| 0 | 1 | 2 | 3 | 4 | 5 | 6 | 7 | 8 | 9 | 10 | 11 | 12 | 13 | 14 |

Stand on 2   Jump 1   Land on ☐

Stand on 8   Jump 1   Land on ☐

| 0 | 1 | 2 | 3 | 4 | 5 | 6 | 7 | 8 | 9 | 10 | 11 | 12 | 13 | 14 | 15 | 16 |

Start on	Jump _____	Land on

 Throw 3 dice.   **1 + 3 + 4 = 8**

More and less

 Overall learning objectives

- Work out how many more are needed to make a larger number and how many to take away to make a smaller number.
- The vocabulary of addition and subtraction.
- Find a total by counting on when one group of objects is hidden.
- Solve simple mathematical puzzles in a practical context.
- Select two groups of objects to make a given total.
- Number bonds to 5/10.

LESSON ONE
HOW MANY MORE?

 Assessment Focus

- Can the children work out how many objects are needed to make a larger number?

 Resources

- cubes or bean bags
- green paper leaves
- number cards

 Oral work and mental calculation

Number bonds

- Use number rhymes as a basis for number bonds, for example '10 fat sausages, 4 in this pan and 6 in the other pan'. (Make sure that by the end of the year children know numbers bonds to 10 fluently.)

 Starting point: Whole class

- Draw some bugs on the board and ask children to come up and make the spots total 5. *"This bug already has 4 spots, so how many more does it need?"*
- Demonstrate a circle game where you have around 5 bugs (cubes or bean bags) and you

count them with the children, then hide all of them behind your back or in a box. Then show just some of them. *"I have 5 bugs altogether and you can see these 3. How many are still hiding behind my back?"* Repeat this several times using a wide range of language for addition and subtraction. *"3 here and another 2 behind my back."*

- Then let each child choose a number of cubes to have as bugs. (Each child should have all the same colour cubes but a different colour from children nearby.) Go around the circle asking how many bugs each child has. Invite a child to write the number on the board, then ask him or her to hide some of their bugs behind their back (this is easier than a box) and just show a few. The other children have to say how many are still hiding.
- Demonstrate anything on the photocopiable activity sheets that children might need help with, such as the recording on Activity sheet 2.

 Group activities

 Focus group

Play a game such as that in the whole-class starter or on Activity sheet 3, with green paper leaves and cubes for bugs. Assess how well the children can use the language of addition and subtraction and their fluency with adding and subtracting, for example *"3 and 6 more makes 9"* or *"9 take away 3 leaves 6"*. Some children might be ready for more abstract recording, using tallies and finding appropriate number cards. Follow one number through to find several different ways of splitting it up. *"8 can be split into 7 and 1 and 6 and 2. Can we find a different way?"* Remember to include 8 and zero.

 Teacher independent groups

Use the photocopiable activity sheets.

- **Activity sheet 1:** The children have to draw in more spots to make the number in the box. You or the child can choose the number for the second half of the page.

More and less

✦ **Activity sheet 2:** In the second half of this sheet you should draw the number of bugs in the boxes that the children can work with according to their experience. It might be useful to give them the bugs and boxes from the whole-class starter activity to work with.

✦ **Activity sheet 3:** You might want to provide green paper leaves and bugs (cubes) to help these children. The lowest leaf is still for 8 bugs but the children have to make up their own 'sum'.

✦ *Plenary session*

✦ Ask someone from each group to show the class what they have found out.

✦ Say *"What is the number in this box? Everyone write that number in the air. So how many spots did you need to add to make them up to 5? So we know that 2 and 3 more makes 5 altogether."*

✦ *"Fiona chose to work with 7 bugs. She can see 4. Tell us how many are hiding."*

✦ *"Hamish had 10 ladybirds on his leaf and 3 were hiding. How many could he see? Who can make that into a number sentence using the word 'add.' What other way of splitting 10 could Hamish try?"*

LESSON TWO HOW MANY LESS?

✦ *Assessment focus*

✦ Can the children work out how many fewer?

✦ *Resources*

✦ cubes
✦ two ponds (bowls of water or drawn on paper)
✦ play dough
✦ containers of toys

✦ *Oral work and mental calculation*

Number bonds to 5/10

✦ Play 'ping pong 5' (slowly and all together at first until children are very confident). You say *"ping"* and they have to respond by saying *"pong"*. Teach them to respond to you saying a number, for example you say *"three"* and they say the number that makes it up to 5 (*"two"*). You say another number, such as *"one"* and they say *"four"* and so on. When they are familiar

with all the number bonds, start to go a little faster, sometimes saying *"ping"* between the numbers. (This keeps up the pace and gets attention.) Then change the game so that sometimes you say specific numbers to individuals for them to reply to, but be sure only to ask those that are confident. When most are very confident, play the game in pairs, then finally, going around the circle – but do this slowly otherwise you risk loss of self-esteem and fear of maths.

✦ *Starting point: Whole class*

✦ Give each child a few cubes to make into a 'train' of a different colour and a different number from those next to them. You have 5 cubes and start by pointing to who has fewer cubes than you. *"I have 5, but Jess only has 2 so she has fewer than me."* Put the trains next to each other and show how 2 is less than 5. Help children to count how many fewer. Go around the circle with children comparing their cube train with the child next to them. *"Kate has 5 and Jake has 3. Jake has 2 fewer than Kate."* As they become familiar with the language of 'fewer' and 'less than', start to show how, if Jake has 2 fewer than Kate, she has 2 more than him, so that the children start to see the relationship.

✦ Focus on individual children with specific questions so you can assess individual progress.

More and less

 ## Group activities

Focus group

Repeat the starter activity with other numbers so you can assess children's understanding and their ability to make number sentences using a wide range of language. *"3 is 1 fewer than 4."* and *"4 is 2 less than 6."*

 ### Teacher independent groups

◆ **Group 1:** Provide two ponds (water in bowls or drawn on paper) and some play dough to make ducks. Say *"Put some ducks on one pond and put fewer on the other pond."*

"How many different ways can you find to split 5 ducks up on 2 ponds?"

◆ **Group 2:** Provide two containers of toys and ask which container has fewer toys. (If the one with more in is smaller with smaller objects, that would make the task more challenging.) Ask the children to count them to see if they were right.

◆ **Group 3:** Challenge this group to find out if there are fewer boys than girls at school today. They could draw a picture to show what they found out.

 ## Plenary session

◆ *"Jackie has 4 ducks and 5 ducks. She says 4 is fewer than 5. How many fewer?"*

◆ *"What is 1 less than 4? Work that out on your fingers. What is 1 less than 2?"*

◆ *"I've got 3 fingers up on this hand and 1 on this hand. Point to the hand with fewer fingers up. How many fewer?"*

◆ *"Group 2 found out that 9 is fewer than 12. Let's count back from 12 on the number line."*

◆ *"Group 3 say that there are fewer girls here today. There are 13 girls and 17 boys. Let's find those numbers on the number line."*

◆ *"What have you learned about today? What shall we try hard to remember for tomorrow?"*

 ## Further activities

◆ Lesson One needs to be repeated frequently as it forms a secure basis for children to develop their own understanding of the link between addition and subtraction and the related language. White out the numbers on Activity sheets 2 and 3 and use them with numbers at least up to 10 by the end of Reception.

◆ Play simple adding and taking away games, keeping score. For example tossing bean bags into a box, scoring 1 or 2 for each one that lands in the box.

 ## Extension

◆ Using cubes, how many different ways can the children find to split up 10, including 10 and 0?

Be ready for a child to say 9 red and 1 blue is different from 9 blue and 1 red.

 ## Support

◆ Use Generic sheet 3 (page 92) to give children practice with different numbers, but also let them record splits of numbers in their own way. Give them plenty of practical work with different objects, such as making necklaces with 10 beads on each one, but in two different colours. *"How many blue and how many green?"*

◆ Give each child a target number on a card and explain that they must make cube trains with that total only, in two colours, for example with 5 they use 3 red and 2 yellow.

✦ Spots on bugs ✦

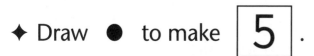

✦ Draw ● to make ⬛ 5 .

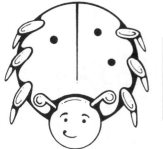 ⬜ spots

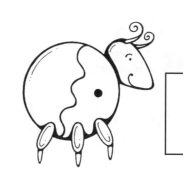 ⬜ spots

 ⬜ spots

 ⬜ spots

✦ Draw ● to make

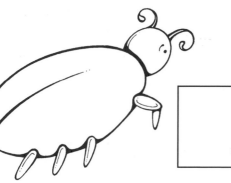 ⬜ spots

 ⬜ spots

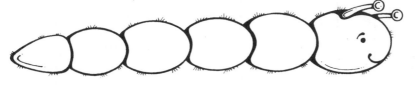  spots

 Draw more bugs with spots.

Name _____

◆ **How many hiding?** ◆

◆ $\boxed{5}$ bugs in each box. How many are hiding?

I can see $\boxed{2}$

$\square$ hiding

I can see $\square$

hiding

I can see $\square$

hiding

I can see $\square$

hiding

◆ Choose how many. $\square$ bugs

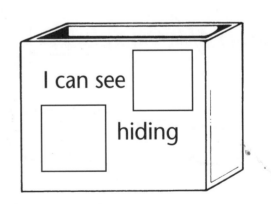

I can see $\square$

hiding

I can see $\square$

hiding

📖 Choose another number and draw more bugs and boxes.

developing
Numeracy Skills

✦ **Bugs on leaves** ✦

✦ | **8** | on each leaf.

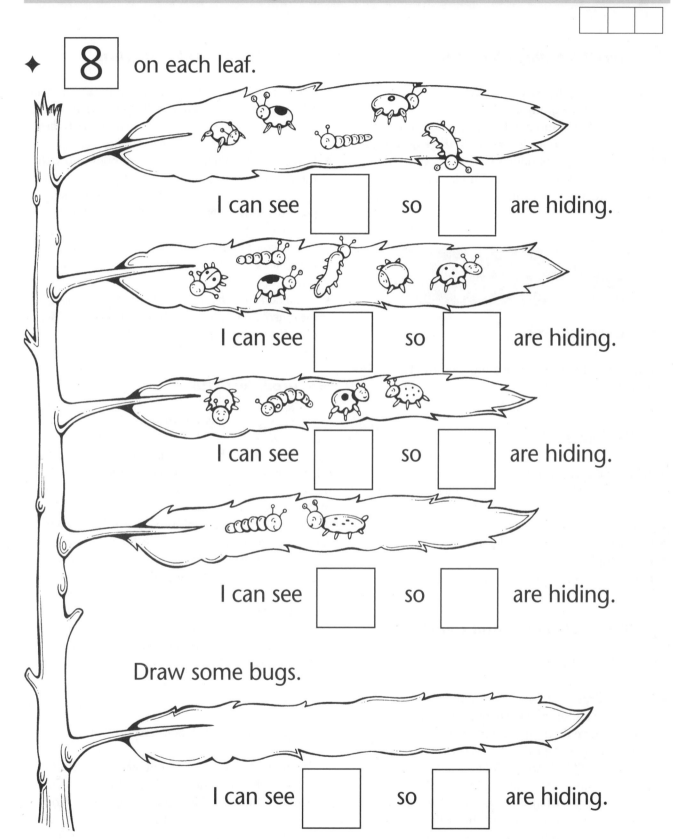

I can see ☐ so ☐ are hiding.

I can see ☐ so ☐ are hiding.

I can see ☐ so ☐ are hiding.

I can see ☐ so ☐ are hiding.

Draw some bugs.

I can see ☐ so ☐ are hiding.

 Choose another number and draw more bugs and leaves.

Separating and combining

 Overall learning objectives

✦ Separate a number of objects into two groups (extend to three groups).
✦ Begin to understand addition as the combination of two groups of objects (extend to three groups).
✦ Use the language of addition.
✦ Use developing mathematical understanding to solve a practical problem.

 **LESSON ONE SEPARATING**

 Assessment focus

✦ Can the children separate a number into two groups, then count?

 Resources

✦ cubes to represent bugs
✦ toy cars (or make cars for bugmobiles with polydrons and so on)
✦ Unifix
✦ paper, card and felt-tipped pens or crayons
✦ play dough
✦ plates

 Oral work and mental calculation

Splitting numbers

✦ Make a 'cube train' with Unifix and ask individual children to come out and count the cubes, or give them practice in counting without touching. *"I have 4 cubes in my cube train. Let's see how I can split it. I can split it into 2 and 2 more. Can you tell me how I can split it another way? When I put the two parts back together again I end up with the number I started with."* Repeat this activity often with different numbers. *"4 can be split into 2 and how many more?"*

 Starting point: Whole class

✦ *"Here are 4 bugs wanting to go to a party and we have 2 bugmobiles. How could we split up the 4 bugs so that some can go in one car and some in another? Is there a different way to do that? Come and show us."*
✦ Let each pair choose a number of bugs and split them into two bugmobiles to go to the party. Send the bugmobiles around the circle so that each pair can show how they would split up their number. *"How many bugs do you have altogether? So we know that if you start with 6 bugs you can split them into 4 and 2, or into 3 and 3. Is there another way?"*
✦ *"Who had enough bugs to put 3 in one car and 4 in the other? How many bugs is that? Jed has 4 in both cars. How many did he start with?"*

 Group activities

 Focus group

Each child should have a collection of cubes that are all the same colour but a different colour from the person next to them. This can prevent cubes getting into the wrong group as you want the children to see that separating and combining doesn't change the number of cubes. Assess them as they count out a number, separating it into two groups, counting each group accurately, then recombining the group. Ask *"Do you need to count?"* (Some children will recognise that in recombining they get back to the number they started with.) Give practice with number bonds as they arise – *"So, 2 and 3 more makes 5 altogether."*

 Teacher independent groups

✦ **Group 1:** This group could make some birthday cards, such as '5 today' and draw pictures with a total of 5 bugs (or ducks and so on). Have ready cut out cars (or ponds and so on). Demonstrate sticking 2 cars on the birthday card and sticking a total of 5 bugs into the 2 cars. Say *"At review time I will ask you about how you split up your bugs."*

Separating and combining

+ **Group 2:** This group could make some play dough buns for the party (maybe 8 or 9 buns), then share them out onto 2 plates and draw what they have done.

+ **Group 3:** These children should work in pairs to repeat the whole class starter activity, working with numbers beyond 10 or 20. They could draw pictures to show what they did.

◆ *Plenary session*

+ Let the focus group talk about what they did. *"I split up 10 into 5 and 5 and into 4 and 6."*
+ Let the other groups show their birthday cards and their drawings. As they do this keep making number sentences – *"10 can be split into 3 and 7 so we know that 3 plus 7 makes 10 altogether."*

◆ *Assessment focus*

+ Can the children combine 2 or 3 groups and count them to find the total?

Resources

+ play dough to make buns
+ paper plates

◆ *Oral work and mental calculation*

Saying the days of the week

+ Chant the days of the week. When the children are fairly confident, chant going around the circle, each child in turn, but support those that need it.
+ Say *"Let's have a party on Friday. This is Monday. How many days to go until Friday? Count on your fingers."*

◆ *Starting point: Whole class*

+ With the children seated in a circle, remind them of Lesson One by demonstrating with play dough buns and plates how to share out numbers (into

two groups of buns at first, then move on to three groups). *"So we can split 10 into 6 and 4. What do you think will happen if we put the 6 and 4 back together again? Yes, we get back to 10 again!"* Work with paper plates, combining two groups of buns onto one plate, counting the total and making a number sentence. You could draw plates on the board as on the activity sheets.

◆ *Group activities*

 Focus group

Use this session to work on the language of addition and ability to make number sentences. Use paper plates and buns, splitting then recombining groups. Make some of this more abstract. *"Make a picture in your head of 2 buns on a plate, then another plate with 3 buns. Make a picture of them now all on the same plate. How many buns altogether?"* (Extend this to combining three groups.)

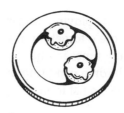 

Separating and combining

 Teacher independent groups

Use the photocopiable activity sheets.

✦ **Activity sheet 1:** Give the children paper plates and play dough buns to work with so that they can combine the numbers, draw the total number of buns on the big plate and write the number.

✦ **Activity sheet 2:** You could draw in more buns on the plates if some of these children are ready to work with larger numbers.

✦ **Activity sheet 3:** This activity moves on to combining the number of buns on three plates. Group 2 can use this sheet when they are ready to combine numbers.

 Plenary session

✦ Talk about the combining of 2 and 3 numbers to make a larger number. *"So if you have 4 buns and another 5, it makes 9 buns altogether. Shut your eyes and make a picture of that in your mind."*

✦ Let the children talk about the numbers they chose. Some children can hold up the numbers with their fingers to check totals.

✦ *"What is 4 buns and 2 more? Add 3 and 1. 3 and 3 together makes how many?"*

✦ *"What did you enjoy doing in maths today?"*

✦ *"Tell me something you know about adding."*

 Further activities

✦ Play 'finger wizz'. Two children come out and on the count of 1, 2, 3, they bring their hands out from behind them holding up their choice of fingers. So if one child holds up 3 and the other holds up 2, everyone has to count the fingers to find how many. As the children get more experienced, let them count on their own and then ask how many fingers altogether. Ask them to say a number sentence, for example *"4 and 3 more makes 7 altogether"*. Vary the language that you use – *"4 plus 3 equals 7"* and *"4 and 3 more makes 7"* and so on.

✦ Vary the game 'finger wizz' by playing 'finger wizz target' where you choose a target number, such as 5 and see how many times in one minute (set a timer) two children can bring out fingers that total 5. Introduce a fist to mean zero.

✦ Have a very simple party, perhaps just with drinks and biscuits. Talk about what needs to be found out, such as who likes orange and who likes lemon best, choice of biscuit or sandwiches. How could we find out?

 Extension

✦ Choose some numbers of buns that share evenly. Does 20/40/50/100 share evenly into two groups?

 Support

✦ Give plenty of practice with splitting up and combining numbers from 4 to 10 so that the children become fluent with the language of addition and are starting to remember simple number facts, such as 3 and 1 more. Use Generic sheet 3 (page 92).

Name _____

✦ How many buns? ✦

✦ Draw the buns on the big plate and count them.

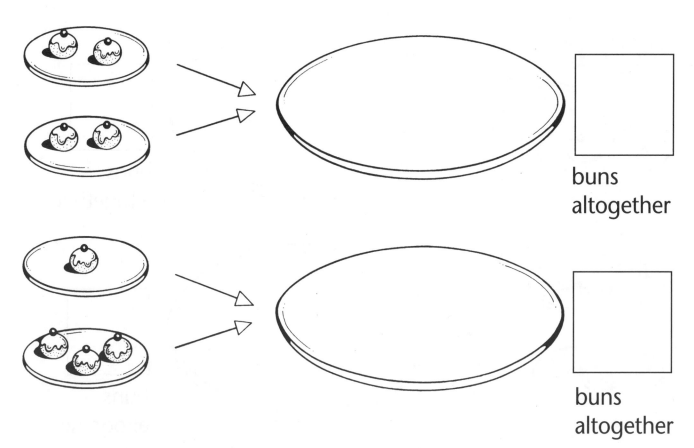

buns
altogether

buns
altogether

✦ Choose how many buns.

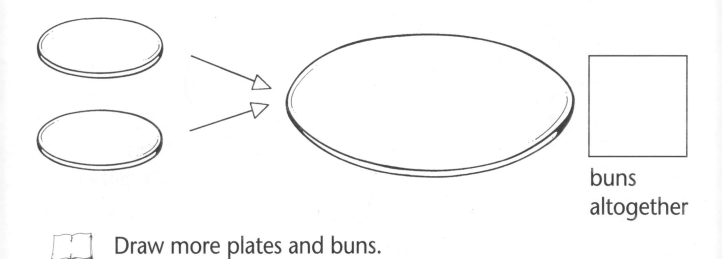

buns
altogether

 Draw more plates and buns.

45

Name _____

✦ Draw the buns on the big plate and count them.

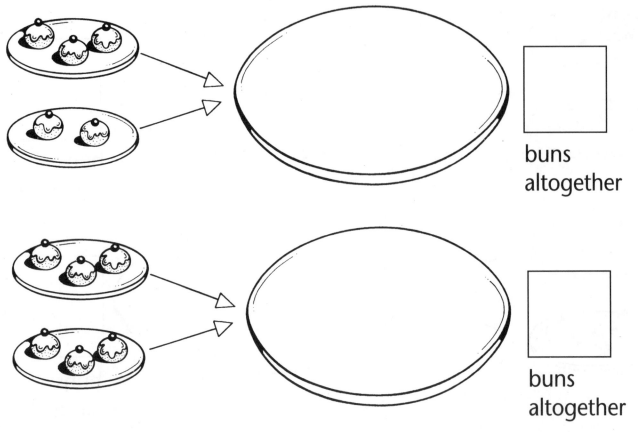

buns
altogether

buns
altogether

✦ Choose how many buns.

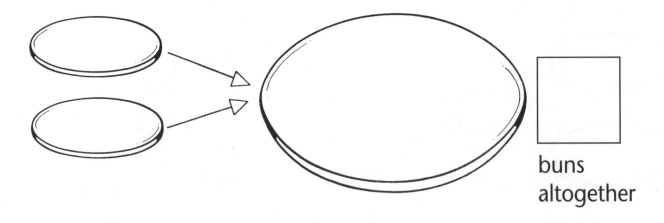

buns
altogether

 Draw more plates and buns.

✦ How many buns? ✦

✦ Draw the buns on the big plate and count them.

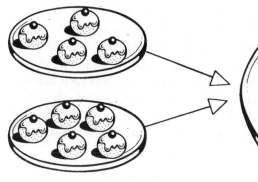 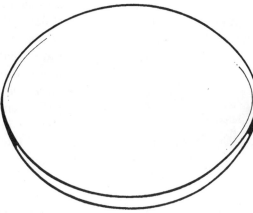 

buns
altogether

✦ Choose how many buns.

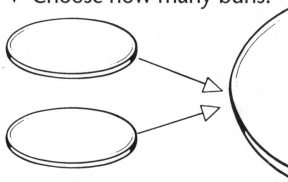

buns
altogether

✦ Now have 3 plates of buns.

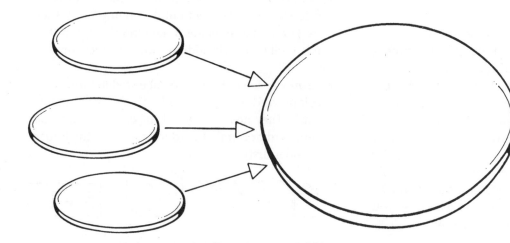 

buns
altogether

 Do it with 3 plates again.

Addition

 ## Overall learning objectives

✦ Begin to understand addition as counting on.
✦ Begin to recognise the addition of doubles by counting on.

**LESSON ONE
THE FEWEST STEPS**

 ## Assessment focus

✦ Can the children see that, when adding two numbers, putting the larger number first involves fewer steps?

 ## Resources

✦ cubes or teddy counters
✦ a floor number line
✦ number cards

 ## Oral work and mental calculation

Number sentences

✦ To prepare for this session ask those that need further experience of counting to prepare some 'cube trains', 3 or 4 each of 1–6 (for number bonds of 6). Hold up a cube train – say of 4 cubes – and ask the children to work out who has one that makes it up to 6. Use a wide range of language for calculating. Then play around the circle, each child making a number sentence. For example, *"I've got 3 so I can make 6 with Peter's 3 because 3 add 3 makes 6."* Establish that 4 and 2 and 2 and 4 both have the answer 6 because you can do adding in any order you choose.

 ## Starting point: Whole class

✦ Stand around the large floor number line and explain that this game is about taking the fewest

steps. Demonstrate starting on 4, counting on 1 and then starting on 1, counting on 4, with two children doing the jumps on the number line. Establish that the number you end on is 5 both times. *"But who did the fewest jumps?"* Do a few more examples, using a wide range of language.

✦ *"Shut your eyes and think of the number line in your head. Think which way round will mean the fewest jumps. 6 jump on 1 land on 7, or 1 jump on 6 land on 7?"* Establish that if you start with the larger number first, you do the fewest hops.

 ## Group activities

 Focus group

Show the children how they can hold the larger number in their head and then just count on with the smaller number. Say *"5 add on 3 more. I hold the 5 in my head and count (use fingers) 6, 7, 8."* Do lots more of these with this focus group, using the floor number line when necessary to demonstrate.

 Teacher independent groups

✦ **Group 1:** Give this group cubes/teddies of two colours and ask them to make adding sums, such as 2 and 1 more makes 3. Remind them that they must tell you their adding sums at review time.

✦ **Group 2:** Give this group cubes/teddies in two colours and some sum cards (5 + 2 =) or number cards. They have to lay out the cubes to show the sum card or number card (always with the larger number first).

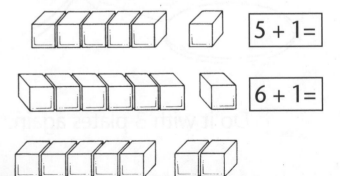

Addition

◆ **Group 3:** Give this group some sum cards that need reversing to make the larger number come first, such as '2 + 8 =' and '1 + 10 =', including several cards with + 10 on them. Ask them to reverse the numbers and make cube trains to show the sums.

◆ Plenary session

◆ Review the '5 and a bit' and '10 and a bit' activities by focusing on not counting from 1 each time. Ask the children to hold up their cubes, or 5 fingers on one hand and 2 on the other. Ask how many? Observe carefully who is tending to start from 1 each time. Say to them *"We can just say 'Hold the 5 in my head and count on 1, 2 more to make 7.'"*

◆ Establish that, if you start with the larger number first when you are adding, you do the fewest jumps and you can work out the answer quickly. If you start from 1 each time (or the smaller number of the two) it is a very slow process. *"So when we are adding, we put the larger number first, hold that in our head and count on the rest of the jumps."*

◆ Many children will need repeated practice of this at mental maths time.

LESSON TWO DOUBLES

◆ Assessment focus

◆ Can the children begin to recognise the addition of doubles by counting on?

◆ Resources

◆ dominoes
◆ number cards

◆ Oral work and mental calculation

Doubling

◆ Do doubling using fingers. For example, 3 on one hand and 3 on the other. Say *"3 count on 3: 4, 5, 6 – 3 add 3 is 6"*. Keep repeating the numbers until most children can remember some doubles.

◆ Hold up fingers on both hands, sometimes a double, sometimes not. The children must count the fingers, say 3 on one hand and 2 on the other and say the answer (or hold up the relevant number card). If the number you are holding up is a double they can say (in a silly voice, or shout, if manageable) *"2 count on 2: 3, 4. Double 2 is 4"*. To calm them down again they should use whispers for the next one – *"4 count on 4: 5, 6, 7, 8. Double 4 is 8"*.

◆ Starting point: Whole class

◆ Remind the children of the counting on they did in Lesson One. If they still need help with counting on, repeat the oral game with cube trains from Lesson One, this time using doubles. So, if you hold up a 3, you ask who can make double 3, and so on.

◆ Group activities

Focus group

Use a copy of Activity sheet 3 with this group teaching them to hold the first number in their heads.

Addition

 Teacher independent groups

Use the photocopiable activity sheets.

 Activity sheet 1: This is a straightforward counting activity. These children could use dominoes to help them to identify the doubles and to draw double 5 or double 6.

✦ **Activity sheet 2:** This activity sheet helps to consolidate doubles to 12. Again, the children could use dominoes to help them.

✦ **Activity sheet 3:** The first part of this sheet asks the children to think of their own numbers to double. Ask them to choose numbers between 10 and 20. You might like to choose the numbers individual

children can work with. The second part of the sheet asks them to work with even higher numbers. You might prefer to white these out and choose your own numbers, especially where children are capable of working beyond 100.

✦ *Plenary session*

✦ Identify the doubles on the dominoes.
✦ Go over the numbers where doubles need to be learned. *"What is double 2?"* and so on. *"When you double this number you have 6. What is the number?"*
✦ Establish that when you are adding, you are counting on along the number line, moving towards the larger numbers. Counting back is going the other way towards 0.

✦ *Further activities*

✦ Do more work on holding the larger number in your head when adding as in Lesson One. Remind the children to reverse the numbers where necessary so they always start with the larger number. Ask them to make a picture of the number line, or cubes, or fingers in their head. (It is very important that we encourage children to develop their mental images so that they have secure mental methods of calculating.)
✦ Say *"What could we do first if we wanted to add 2 and 7 more? That's right, it is quicker to put the 7 in our head, then count on our fingers, 8, 9. 2 count on 7 is 9 and 7 count on 2 is 9."*
✦ Play 'Finger wizz' (see Chapter 6) and see how many times in one minute they make doubles with their fingers.

✦ *Extension*

✦ Find doubles and halves of amounts of money, using coins and a number line.

✦ *Support*

 Use Generic sheet 4 (page 93) to give more practice with counting to 6. Write the numbers

1 to 6 at the bottom. Two children share a sheet, one plays one side of the central line using the numbers at the top, and one the other side working up from the bottom. They take it in turns to throw a dice, count the spots on the dice, match that to a number on their side of the sheet and write that number (or put a cube or colour a square). The first to throw a number five times is the winner.

✦ This sheet can also be used to practise number bonds to 6 using cubes of two colours, so 5 + 1 and 4 + 2 make 6.

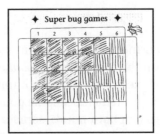

Name _____

✦ Find the doubles ✦

✦ Count then put a ✔ by the doubles. Write the numbers.

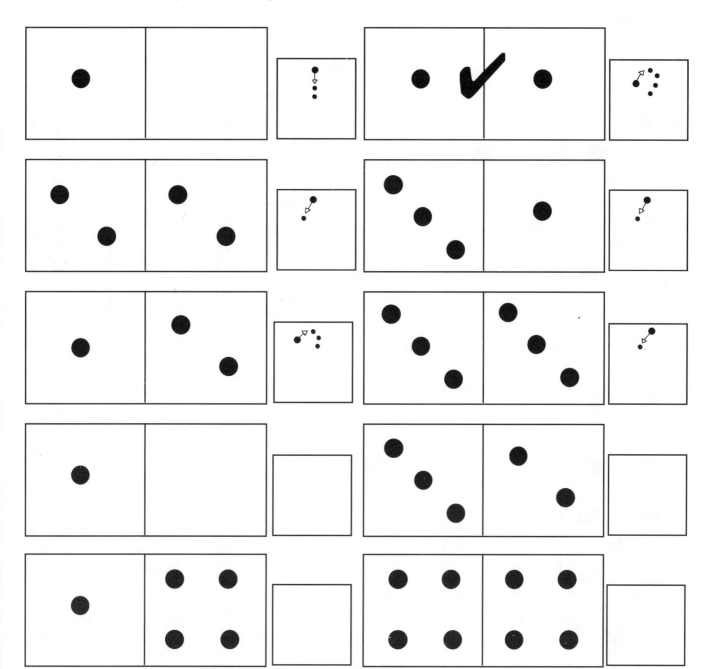

✦ Draw a double domino.

Numeracy
Reception/P1

developing
Numeracy Skills

Photocopiable
©Hopscotch Educational Publishing
51

✦ Double dominoes ✦

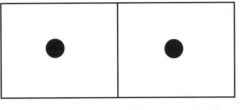

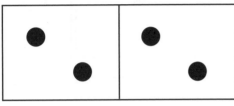

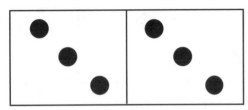

double 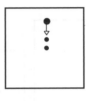 is

double 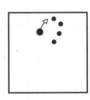 is

double 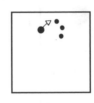 is

✦ Draw dots to make doubles.

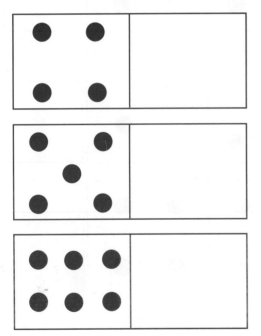

double is

double is

double is

 Double more numbers.

52 **Numeracy**
Reception/P1

developing
Numeracy
Skills

Photocopiable

©Hopscotch Educational Publishing

Name _____

✦ **Double a number** ✦

✦ Put some numbers in your head, then double them.

 is in my head. Double that number makes

 is in my head. Double that number makes

 is in my head. Double that number makes

 is in my head. Double that number makes

 is in my head. Double that number makes

✦ Now do these.   Double 14 is

Double 17 is

 Try with some larger numbers.

   (19)   (20)   (50)

Subtraction

 Overall learning objectives

✦ Begin to understand subtraction as 'taking away', counting how many are left.
✦ Remove a smaller number from a larger one and find how many are left by counting back from the larger number.
✦ Begin to find out how many have been removed from a larger group of objects by counting on from a number.

LESSON ONE
TAKE AWAY STORIES

 Assessment focus

✦ Can the children understand 'take away' and count how many are left?

 Resources

✦ cubes/teddies
✦ trays
✦ sorting toys
✦ play dough
✦ number lines
✦ wooden numbers/number cards
✦ sum cards such as 3 – 1 =

Oral work and mental calculation

Number bonds

✦ Play 'up and down fives'. The children copy your fingers on one hand, some held up and some down. *"Put 2 down, how many up?"* In a circle, one child puts some fingers down and asks the rest of the children to copy and say how many are up or down. Later play with ten fingers.

 "I have 5 fingers altogether, if I fold down 2 how many are up? If you count on 2 from 3 you get to…? If you count back 2 from 4 you get to…? How many fewer than 5 is 3? How many more than 2 is 6?"

Starting point: Whole class

✦ (You will probably want to teach this lesson over a few sessions.) Make up some number stories with children using cubes, teddies or other such resources. Tell stories such as *"There were five mice eating the cheese then 3 ran away, how many left?"* or *"Gran made 6 buns and Alec ate 1, how many were left?"* Let some children come and take away an object and count how many are left. Use a variety of contexts for the stories and make a display to help the children read words so that they are ready for the activity sheets in Lesson Two.
✦ Let children go to the front and make up stories of their own. Make sentences together using the words 'take away'.
✦ Now (or later) show children how they can represent 'take away' by crossing out objects on a drawing.

 Group activities

 Focus group

Make up number stories together using 'take away' and check that each child can count how many are left and then make a number sentence '7 take away 4 leaves 3.' The children need to move on to being able to find how many are left from counting back from the larger number, or counting on from the smaller. You can do this by going over the 'How many hiding?' activity sheet from Chapter 6, Lesson One. Some children are likely to count on, others will count back. Let them talk about what they do in their head.

 Teacher independent groups

✦ **Group 1:** Provide sorting toys, play dough and trays to make up take away stories.

54
©Hopscotch Educational Publishing

developing
Numeracy
Skills

Numeracy
Reception/P1

Subtraction

◆ **Group 2:** These children can do the same as those in Group 1 but they should be given actual numbers to work with. For example, they could be set the following challenge: You have made 12 jam tarts for a party and the Knave of Hearts comes and steals some. Provide them with number cards and a number line to at least 20. Ask them to draw pictures of their take away stories.

◆ **Group 3:** Select a task that uses numbers to challenge children, for example: There were 32 jam tarts and the Knave of Hearts ate 17 of them. Draw a picture of your number story.

◆ *Plenary session*

◆ Ask some of the children to come to the front and tell their number stories. Some of them might be able to hold up sum cards as they tell the story. Talk through the different number stories. Say *"Mark, there were 6 buns and 4 were eaten, so how many were left? Can you make a take away number sentence?"*

◆ *"Tell me something you learned today in maths."*

◆ LESSON TWO TAKING AWAY ◆

◆ *Assessment focus*

◆ Can the children count back from and up to a number and see that both ways give the same answer?

◆ *Resources*

◆ cubes/teddies
◆ number cards
◆ a tray and a cloth
◆ an assortment of familiar objects

◆ *Oral work and mental calculation*

Subtraction stories

◆ Tell number stories such as *"There were 5 funny clowns (hold up fingers) playing in the hall and one of them fell over his big feet and had to go to hospital. How many clowns left playing?"*

◆ Let the children make up their own stories in pairs then go around the circle telling them. Develop this over the year so that they can come and pick

out the number cards (and eventually the symbols) used in their stories.

◆ *Starting point: Whole class*

◆ Do a circle game, demonstrating first by having 5 teddies/cubes in front of you and taking away 2. Ask the children to tell you how they know how many are left. Some will physically count the teddies by pointing, others might use fingers. Some might do the calculation in their head and others will 'just know'.

◆ When they are confident, give out some cubes/teddies and go around the circle with the children taking some away and telling their number story. Move on to doing the counting in two different ways in order to establish that whether you count on or back, you end up with the same number. *"There are 7 teddies and 3 hide so 4 are left. Let's count up from 4 until we get to 7. 4 teddies (show 4 fingers), let's count up from 4: 5 (hold up a finger), 6, 7. So, from 4 count up to 7 is 3. Now let's start with the 7. There were 7 teddies, there are only 4 now. 7 is in my head, let's count back to 4 together, 6, 5, 4. Let's say together, 7 count back 3 makes 4."*

◆ Revisit some of the number stories from Lesson One so that the children are ready for the activity sheets. Remind them about crossing out objects to help them to take them away.

Subtraction

♦ Group activities

Focus group

Have some familiar objects on a tray, count them together and cover them with a cloth. Take some away, sometimes by showing the children how many you took away so they must work out how many are left under the cloth. At other times hide what you take away, but show what is left on the tray. When children have enough experience, show them the number sentence for these on the number line. (Introduce them to symbols by the end of the year.)

Teacher independent groups

Use the photocopiable activity sheets.

♦ **Activity sheet 1:** The children can use play dough buns they have made earlier to help them to do this activity sheet. (The hand shows how many are eaten.)

♦ **Activity sheet 2:** Children have to write the numbers and on the last one cross out how many are taken away as well.

♦ **Activity sheet 3:** For the lower section you can suggest numbers.

♦ Plenary session

♦ Ask some children from each group to show their number stories on the activity sheets, assessing who is confident with 'take away'. *"So how much is 10 take away 8? Can you tell me another take away sentence?"*

♦ Demonstrate a subtraction number story with a line of children. For example, *"There are 10 children in the line, 6 have dark hair. How many children don't have dark hair? Did you work that out by counting on or counting back?"* Ask them to tell you what is special about counting on and counting back to do take aways. (You get the same answer.)

♦ Further activities

♦ Make a spider-eating monster from a folded-over piece of card and a long strip of card with 6 spiders on it. Make sure the monster is long enough to get all 6 spiders inside. Use this at oral maths time.

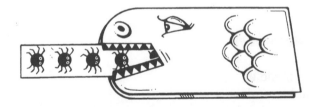

♦ Extension

♦ Play 'Beat the calculator' with take away sum cards. The children are in two groups; one group has a calculator and *must* key in the calculation; the other group must do the calculation mentally. Turn over a calculation card, such as 3 – 2. The group to answer first wins the point. (The non-calculator group almost always wins!)

♦ Support

♦ Many children are likely to need repeated activities with taking away from small numbers to take away and counting the remainder. The 'How many hiding?' activity sheet in Chapter 6 Lesson One can be done in several contexts and children asked to draw what they did.

✦ How many buns? ✦

✦ Make the number stories.

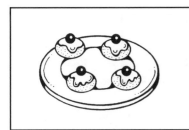  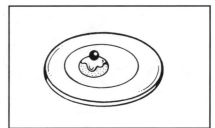

| 4 | buns , | eat | | leaves | |

| | buns , | eat | | leaves | |

| | buns , | eat | | leaves | |

✦ Draw more buns.

 buns , eat

Name _____

◆ How many left? ◆

◆ Look at the pictures and finish the number stories.

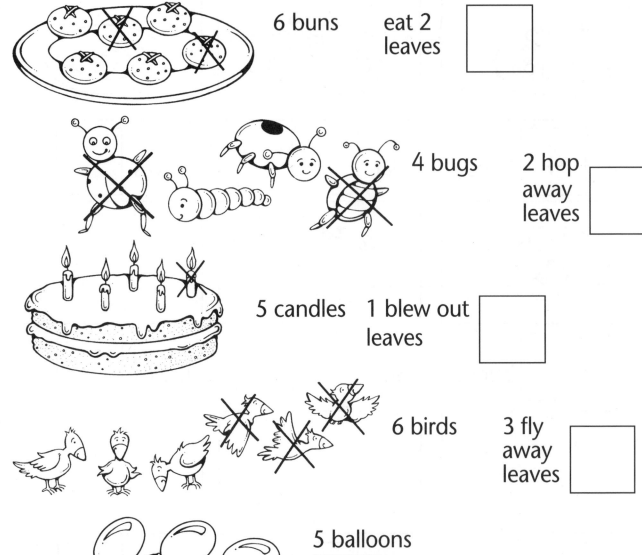

6 buns   eat 2 leaves

4 bugs   2 hop away leaves

5 candles   1 blew out leaves

6 birds   3 fly away leaves

5 balloons   pop   leaves

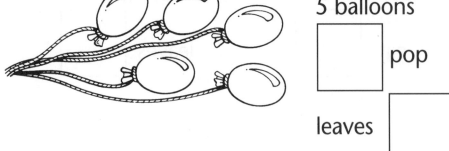

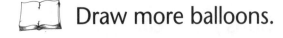 Draw more balloons.

Name _____

✦ **Taking away** ✦

✦ Finish these take away number stories.

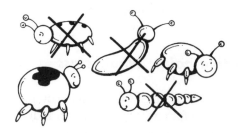   5 take away 3 leaves ☐

   ☐ take away 4 leaves ☐

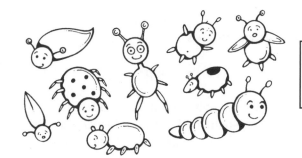   ☐ take away ☐ leaves ☐

✦ Draw some more.

 Do some with big numbers.

Calculation strategies

Overall learning objectives

- Further practice with addition as counting on.
- Understand that they do not need to start at 1 each time when counting on.
- Begin to recognise + and = symbols.
- Use their knowledge to develop calculation strategies.
- To be able to explain their strategies.

LESSON ONE
DON'T COUNT FROM 1!

Assessment focus

- Can the children understand that they do not need to count from 1 each time?

Resources

- cubes
- calculators
- sum cards, such as 2 + 1 = and 5 + 5 =

Oral work and mental calculation

Number bonds

- Do some finger adding, such as "1 on this hand, 1 on the other hand; 1 and 1 makes 2." Explain that they do not need to count from one each time – "There are 5 on this hand and 1 on this hand, how many altogether? Do we need to count this 5 on this hand? Is it still 5? Now let's have 5 on this hand and 2 more. How many?"

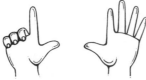

"We know that there are 5 fingers on this hand because we counted it last time, so we don't need to count it again. So let's count on: 6, 7, …"

- Assess who is aware of the + and = symbols on a calculator. Hold up a sum card and see who can read it. Slowly and carefully, explain how to put calculations into the calculator.

Starting point: Whole class

- Give each child 5 cubes. Count them carefully, making a tally for each one. Establish that everyone has the same number, no-one has fewer, or more. Then pass around a pot of cubes so that the children can take a few out in turns. "Lizzy took out 3 more. She started with 5 and now she has 3 more. Wait, we don't need to count that 5 again, do we. Let's just count the extra 3, so we have 5 in our head, then 6, 7, 8 so we have 8 cubes altogether."
- Allow as much practice as possible talking about their calculations as this lays a firm foundation for later work on flexible methods of calculating.

Group activities

Focus group

Repeat the starter activity again using different numbers, giving each child individual teaching to make sure they all have experience of not counting from 1 each time.

Teacher independent groups

- **Group 1:** Provide this group with sum cards from 6 to 10 and show them how to set out cubes as '5 and a bit'. "6 is a 5 train and 1 more. 7 is a 5 train and 2 more" and so on. They should make cube trains and draw them. You will use these for calculating at review time.

- **Group 2:** This group should do the same as Group 1 but ask them to record their numbers in some way as well as drawing cubes.

- **Group 3:** This group should do a similar activity to Group 2 but using '10 and a bit' with cards 11–20.

developing **Numeracy Skills**

Calculation strategies

✦ Plenary session

✦ *"Look, Emmie has 5 green cubes and 2 more. Who can add that quickly in their head? Now let's hold up 5 and 2 more fingers. We don't need to count from 1. Put the 5 in your head and count 2."*

✦ *"George has 5 green, 5 yellow and then 1 more green. How many? How did you work that out?"*
✦ Observe carefully who is still tending to count from 1 each time.

✦ LESSON TWO
HOW DID YOU DO IT?

✦ Assessment focus

✦ Can the children talk about what they do with numbers?

✦ Resources

✦ a copy of Generic sheet 5 (page 94) drawn on the board
✦ some coloured chalk
✦ number cards up to 6

✦ Oral work and mental calculation

Calculating doubles

✦ Do some mental maths practice on doubles (and halves) to 10 or 20. Invite two children to hold up the same number of fingers for counting. Use a wide range of language. *"Double 4 is 4 and another 4. 2 lots of 2 makes 4 altogether. If double 3 is 6, what is half of 6?"*

✦ Starting point: Whole class

✦ Draw a large copy of Generic sheet 3 on the board with numbers suitable for your children. Play this

simple three in a row game with the class divided into two teams, with one child chosen as scribe. Each scribe will use a different-coloured chalk. Decide on a starting number, such as 5. Ask a child to choose a number from the box. Each time a number is taken from the box it is added to the starting number. So if the starting number is 5 and the number taken from the box is 2, the numbers are added and the scribe can colour one of the bugs with 7 on. The idea is to get three numbers of one colour together in a row in any direction. It is worth playing this game many times to give repeated help with number bonds. (Use zero before children go into Y1/P2.) Each time an answer is given, ask how they did it in their head. (If a calculation is wrong, write it on the board and ask who agrees.) *"Now in your groups I want you to think carefully when you are doing your sums so that you tell us about what you were thinking in your head when you did them."*

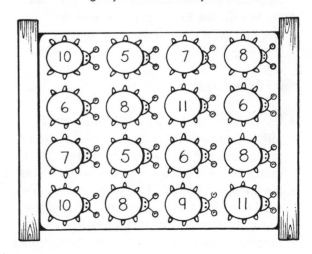

Numeracy
Reception/P1

developing
Numeracy
Skills

61

©Hopscotch Educational Publishing

Calculation strategies

✦ Group activities

Focus group

Use a variety of apparatus and ask the children to make up 'sums' and tell you what they do. Give prompts to use a wide range of language. *"4 take away 2 leaves you with 2. 6 and 4 more makes 10. Start on 5 on the number line and jump 5 – you land on 10."* Encourage more able children to use numbers above 10 and keep observing if children need help not to count from 1 each time.

Teacher independent groups

Use the photocopiable activity sheets.

✦ **Activity sheet 1:** Remind the children in this group that they don't have to start at 1 every time as the 5 fingers are the same each time. Stress that they must form their numbers carefully from the top.

✦ **Activity sheet 2:** Remind children they don't always need to count from 1 each time.

✦ **Activity sheet 3:** The explanation of how this sheet works is given in the whole-class starting point on page 61. The children work in pairs using two different colours of cubes. Ask them to record in their own way how many times they win with three a row. Remind them to check each other's calculations. There is a blank version of this sheet on page 94 which will allow you to play the game using different numbers.

✦ Plenary session

✦ Give children plenty of support to talk about what they did with calculations. *"Katie said she has pictures of teddies in her mind to add them. Bobbie closes his eyes and sees a picture of a number line. Jake used his fingers."* Ask *"Did you need to count from one when you added 5 fingers and 4 more?"*

✦ Go over Activity sheet 1 with all the children, in order, continually reminding them that the 5 fingers remain the same each time so they do not need to be counted.

✦ Further activities

✦ Play 'beat the calculator' (see page 56). This helps children to learn the symbols +, – and =.

✦ Put calculators in role play areas so that children get a sense of what the keys do.

✦ Extension

✦ Use Generic sheet 4 (page 93) for a paired tallying game. The children throw the dice and make one tally in each square on their sheet to match the dice thrown, so a throw of 3 means one tally in 3 squares. Play continues in turn until one player has covered their side of the sheet. You can develop this to keeping a running total, so if 3 was the first throw, and 2

was the next, their total is 5. Then a throw of 4 would give a total of 9. Emphasise not counting the squares from 1 each time and that writing the total so far onto the last square counted helps with this.

✦ Support

✦ You might want to do more tallying to give practice in making one mark for each item. Ask a child to come out and 'hold up fingers and we will draw one tally for each finger'. Emphasise that we make 8 tallies for 8 fingers and when we count them, the number we write is the last number in the count. (Watch out for children who count to 8 then say there are 9.)

✦ Don't count from 1 ✦

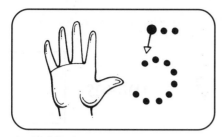 **and 1 more is**

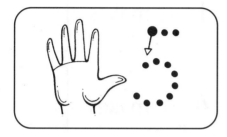 **and 2 more is**

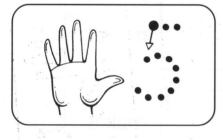 **and 3 more is**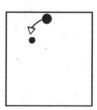

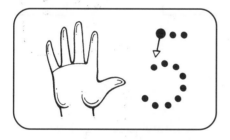 **and 4 more is**

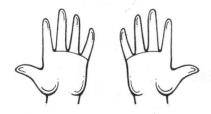 **5 and 5 makes**

  Draw and count more fingers.

✦ **How many?** ✦

5   and   2   makes   ☐

5   and   1   makes   ☐

5   and   4   makes   ☐

5   and   ☐   makes   ☐

5   and   ☐   makes   ☐

✦ You need a dice.

5   and   makes

5   and   ☐   makes   ☐

 Draw your fingers and toes.

Name _____

◆ Make 3 in a row ◆

10 8 9 12

7 9 7 8

11 8 11 9

12 9 12 7

Start with 5

add

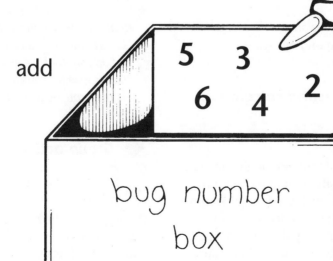

5 3 7
6 4 2

bug number box

developing **Numeracy Skills**

Measuring

Overall learning objectives

✦ Use mathematical language such as more or less, longer or shorter, heavier or lighter.
✦ Compare quantities by making direct comparisons of two then three lengths or masses and filling and emptying containers.

LESSON ONE
GUESS AND CHECK

✦ Assessment focus

✦ Can children use the language of measures to make direct comparisons, reasonable estimates, then checks of length, mass and capacity?

✦ Resources

✦ small boxes of various heights and capacities
✦ ribbon of various thicknesses, string, paper strips, (long, short, wide and narrow/thin)
✦ soft toys, (fat, thin, tall, short, heavy, light)
✦ parcels (heavy and light, (include polystyrene to make a large but light parcel)
✦ a purse full of pennies and one with just a few pence
✦ cubes/teddies/fir cones
✦ newspapers
✦ cups, jugs, bowls in various sizes
✦ balance scales, feely bag and masses

✦ Oral work and mental calculation

Measuring

✦ Do some comparing and making rough guesses, then checking with length, then mass and (on another day) with capacity. Keep doing this until the children have enough experience to move on. Ask two children who are very different in height to stand up. *"Let's guess who is taller."* Make sure they know that this is a guess (or an estimate).

"How can we find out if we are right." Ask the two children to stand back to back. Repeat with two children of similar height.
✦ With everyone in a circle, ask the children to compare the length of their shoes with those of the child next to them. *"Whose shoes are the longest/shortest?"*
✦ Use ribbon or string of different lengths. *"Come and find a bit of string longer than this one."*
✦ *"Which parcel is heavier, this one or this one? Let's guess then weigh them."*
✦ *"Feel both of the masses in the feely bag. Bring out the lighter one."*
✦ *"Find me a cup that would hold more /less than this one. How can we check that you are right?"*
✦ *"Which purse has more?"*
✦ With a varied selection of boxes, or bottles or jugs or bowls, one tall and thin, one wide and fat, make comparisons of capacity in preparation for the starting point (see Activity sheet 3).

Starting point: Whole class

✦ When children have a fairly well-developed sense of the language of measures, do some more demanding activities that will allow you to asses understanding. Sit the children in the circle with a selection of items in the middle and give them some tasks. *"Bring me a ribbon narrower than this one."*, *"Find the shortest paint brush."* or *"Find a strip of paper wider than this one, but not as long."*
✦ In PE do 'guess then check' tasks such as *"Do you think we can get all the children onto this mat?"*, *"Guess how far you can jump."*, *"If we all lay end to end do you think we will reach right across the hall?"*, *"Guess how far you could throw this beanbag."* and *"Is this crate heavier than this one?"*

Group activities

          Focus group

Do assessment tasks, such as guessing then checking weights of parcels and listening to each individual child make direct comparisons of first two, then three items.

Measuring

 Teacher Independent Groups

✦ **Group 1:** Provide varied bottles and containers for sand and water play, including tall and thin bottles. Ask the children to put containers in order of how much they hold. If space is limited set up a mini water play on a metal tray and a mini salt/dry sand play.

✦ **Group 2:** Let children play with balance scales and a wide range of objects to compare. *"Find the thing that is the lightest/heaviest."* This could be in the context of a shop that sells cereal boxes and so on to link with Lesson Two.

✦ **Group 3:** These children should find three cups/mugs/pots that all hold about the same amount and then find how many of those go into a teapot.

Plenary session

✦ Ask the different groups of children to show what they did. Keep emphasising the language of comparison. *"Which held more? How do you know that one held the least? How could we check that this jug holds about 4 cupfuls?"*

LESSON TWO
IS IT STILL THE SAME?

Assessment focus

✦ Can children use the language of comparison: more, less, least, fewer, taller, shorter, heavier, lighter?

Resources

✦ cups and bowls of various sizes
✦ triangles of toast (paper) and two plates
✦ cereal boxes
✦ large labels with the word 'more' written on them

Oral work and mental calculation

Comparing numbers

✦ Use the toast triangles to compare 2 numbers, such as 6 and 2. 6 is 4 more. Then make two lines of toast, both with 5 pieces. Establish that they both have the same number. Space out one line. Ask the children what has happened. Some will say that the line now has more. Count them again and establish that there is still the same number – but a longer line.

Starting point: Whole class

✦ Tell the story of Jack and the beanstalk. Have ready a small and large bowl, two cups and two cereal boxes so that you can do direct comparison, first guessed and then checked. *"Which would be best for the giant's cereal bowl?"* (Keep emphasising the words 'more' and 'less'.) *"Does it hold more than this one? How can we check?"* Use any method for checking – putting something in the bowls and pouring from one to the other. Ask children to think of another way.

✦ Repeat with the two cups and cereal boxes. (Folded newspapers can be put into boxes to compare capacities.)

✦ Show one plate with three pieces of toast and one with about 10. Ask for comparisons then check by counting. *"Put a label 'more' next to the plate that has more."*

Measuring

◆ Group activities

Focus group

Do comparisons of three items, such as putting cubes into three different bowls, first guessing, then checking the capacity. Wide and shallow ice cream containers are deceptive and hold much more than children (and adults!) think.

Teacher independent groups

Use the photocopiable activity sheets.

◆ **Activity sheet 1:** The children could use sand or water or shells/fir cones/cubes to fill the containers. They must show the containers at review time and say which held more.

◆ **Activity sheet 2:** These children have to write the word 'more' in the right places. They then draw more toast for the giant and cakes for Jack and the giant.

◆ **Activity sheet 3:** Provide three small boxes of different sizes and some small objects, such as cubes. The children have to fill each box with the small objects then compare the number that each one holds by counting.

◆ Plenary session

◆ Ask two children from each group to show the class what they have done. Assess the children's use of the language of comparisons by helping them to make a sentence about their work. *"I know this box held more than this one because I could pour all the fir cones from this smaller one into this one and there was still space for more."*

◆ Further activities

◆ Guess the capacity of containers then check with yoghurt pots. It can help to have similar yoghurt pots so you can make a 'real' graph.

The blue jug holds about 5 yoghurt pots full of water but the white one holds almost 9.

◆ Read 'Jim and the beanstalk' by Raymond Briggs for more work on sizes.

◆ Extension

◆ Use the 'real' graph to develop children's thinking. For example, "How many more yogurt pots of water did the white jug hold? So the difference between 9 and 5 is 4. Now find a container that will hold more than the white jug and find out how much more it holds."

◆ Support

◆ Keep doing activities that can be done in a few moments. Say *"Bring me a paint brush longer than this one."*

◆ **Which holds more?** ◆

◆ Find 2

Which holds more? Draw them here.

less	more

◆ Find 2

Which holds more? Draw them here.

less	more

 How many in  ?

◆ Who has more? ◆

◆ Who has more – Jack or the giant?

Write [more] in the right boxes.

Draw more
toast

 Draw for and the

◆ **Measure the boxes** ◆

✦ Find 3 boxes.

✦ Draw them in order.

Tallest – ➔ Shortest

✦ Which box holds the most cubes?
Draw them here.

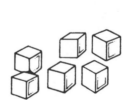 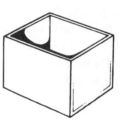

Holds the most – – – – – – – – – – – – – – – – ➔ Holds the least

 Weigh them full. Draw.

Sorting and matching

 Overall learning objectives

✦ Sort and match objects justifying decisions made.
✦ Collect and discuss data and find simple ways to represent it.

LESSON ONE SORTING

 Assessment focus

✦ Can the children sort things into appropriate groups?

 Resources

✦ Blu-Tack
✦ 'The enormous turnip' story
✦ cooking utensils
✦ coloured squares to make graphs
✦ cubes
✦ items for sorting
✦ PE hoops and trays

 Oral work and mental calculation

Counting and data handling

✦ Give children repeated practice with short data-handling activities that also involve counting. *"Stand over here all the children who are 4 years old. How many? Now all the children who are 5 stand here Are more children 4, or are more 5?"* Other ideas are sorting by shoe colour, hair or eye colour and so on.
✦ Later, they could draw and cut out pictures of themselves on squares of paper, then use these to make temporary Venn diagrams and graphs using Blu-Tack, placing themselves appropriately.

We walk to school

We come to school in a car

 Starting point: Whole class

✦ Tell the story of 'The enormous turnip'. You can develop many ideas of size from this story as well as sequencing. Demonstrate weighing and cooking turnips. Let the children taste it to see if they like it. Make a chart, 'we like turnips', and 'we don't like turnips'.
✦ Then make a graph to show this using cubes. Give them experience of a more abstract graph by copying the cube graph with squares of coloured paper. (Use coloured squares of paper for making graphs rather than time-consuming colouring.)

Liked turnips

Didn't like turnips

7 children like turnips, 4 don't

 Group activities

Focus group

Make further diagrams and cube graphs, taking the time to assess understanding with each child. With a small group, the numbers involved in such tasks as 'Who likes corn flakes better than Weetabix?' will be so small that questions such as *"How many more children like Weetabix?"* can be answered by most children. More able children can be asked to gather data, first from this focus group, then later from the whole class, for example 'do more children like salt and vinegar crisps, or ready salted?' Let the children suggest their own ideas.

Teacher independent groups

✦ **Group 1:** Sorting and matching needs to be repeated until the children are confident with it and can count the items involved. Use mostly mathematical things rather than just sorting toys, such as triangles and squares, so that they don't fall behind. Give them a chance to sort by their own criteria.

Sorting and matching

Group 2: Give this group items to sort according to your suggestions, then later, in their own way. Vary the items over several days, for example a collection of boxes that are cuboids, cylinders and other shapes. Use PE hoops and trays to sort the larger items.

Group 3: Give the children a list of around five girls and five boys (including themselves) and then give them a challenge. For example, they could investigate the colours of shoes or clothing and produce a more complex diagram, such as the one on the right.

Plenary session

Look at the work produced by all the groups. Ask questions such as *"Why did you put all those in that group?"* and *"Is there another way that Cindy could have sorted these shapes?"* Do plenty of counting of items in groups as many children will still need counting every day.

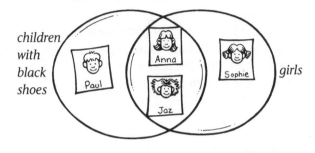

children with black shoes ... *girls*

LESSON TWO
DATA DRAWINGS

Assessment focus

Can the children use a variety of shapes to make pictures, talking about and counting the shapes they have used?

Resources

- 2D shapes (as many sets as possible)
- Logi Blocks
- a feely bag
- Blu-tack

Oral work and mental calculation

Counting and sorting

- Put 2D shapes into a feely bag and take out a handful. Sort them according to shape – 3 triangles, 2 squares, 4 circles.
- Pass the bag around the circle and let a few

children do the same sorting exercise. Draw large squares and make a 'real' graph, sticking the actual shapes onto the squares. Then make representations of the shapes on a graph. Count and compare the numbers as in Lesson One. *"How many more triangles than circles?"* Remember to talk about properties of shapes (the shape with three straight sides) and compare sizes of shapes using Logi Blocks, for example the big red triangle and the small yellow one.

Starting point: Whole class

Demonstrate a simple picture made from 2-D shapes.

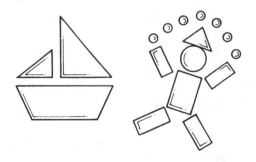

"I need a round shape for the clown's head but I want straight sides for the boat."

Sorting and matching

* Sit the children in a circle and give each pair around five or six different shapes and see if they can make a simple picture with them. Let some children come and select more shapes if they need them, or trade a shape. (You can use a wide variety of shapes including hexagons, pentagons, semi-circles as the children will not just be learning the names, but thinking of the properties of the shapes and how useful they are for their pictures.)
* When the pictures are complete, go around the circle asking how many circles/squares/shapes with six straight sides, and so on, they used. Then demonstrate how to make a 'real' graph with the shapes.

◆ Group activities

Focus group

Repeat the starting activity, making pictures, observing and listening carefully to assess children's language of shape. Then make 'real' graphs with the shapes they have used, and assess understanding as you help them to represent that 'real' graph on paper.

 Teacher independent groups

Use the photocopiable activity sheets.

* **Activity sheet 1:** Help the children with the colour codes for colouring the shapes. They colour and count, then write the numerals.

* **Activity sheet 2:** The graph at the top is a colouring and counting activity. For the picture they can use any number of the three shapes. Record the numbers of shapes used at the bottom of their sheet.

* **Activity sheet 3:** According to the children's ability you could add more shapes at the top of the page. The children should draw their own picture and record how many of each shape they used, making a 'real' graph of them for review time.

◆ Plenary session

* Ask some children to show their completed sheets. Then ask them questions about them.
  "How many circles did you use?"
  "Did you use more circles or more oblongs?"
  "Which shapes did Lisa use for her cat?"

◆ Further activities

* Provide paper shapes on the maths table to fold and colour. Halve paper 2D shapes to make displays.
* Let the children play with 2D and 3D shapes including with Polydrons for construction.
* Circle game: pass around a feely bag. The children feel a shape and describe it, and others have to guess what it is.

◆ Extension

* Sort 2D shapes into two sets that overlap and include a semi-circle in the middle (see right).

◆ Support

* Make sure the children can describe shapes they have played with, for example *"This shape has 6 straight sides."*

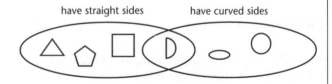

have straight sides   have curved sides

✦ Shape pictures ✦

✦ **Colour.**

red   green   black

✦ **How many shapes?**

How many [rectangle] ? _3_____

How many [triangle] ? _____

How many [circle] ? _____

 Make another picture.

Name _____

◆ Shape pictures ◆

◆ **Colour and count.**

How many?

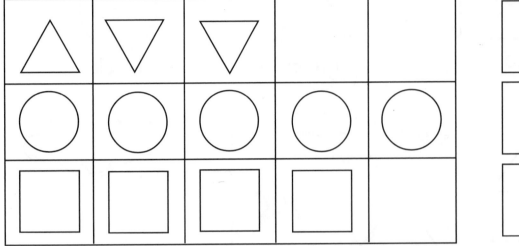

◆ Draw a picture with

📖 How many? __ __ __

✦ Shape pictures ✦

✦ Use these shapes to draw a picture.

I used _____ △

I used _____ ○

I used _____ □

 Make a graph.

Patterns and puzzles

 Overall learning objectives

- Recognise and make simple repeating patterns, including using numbers.
- Count in 2s and 10s.
- Solve simple mathematical puzzles, using different shapes.
- Make predictions.

LESSON ONE
COPY AND CONTINUE

 Assessment focus

- Can the children recognise, copy and continue repeating patterns?

 Resources

- large dotty dice
- 2D and 3D shapes
- examples of patterns
- short and tall bottles
- stamper pens
- cubes
- beads and string
- unbreakable mirrors

 Oral work and mental calculation

Tallying and counting to 20

- Draw three lines of 20 shapes like these.

- The children throw a dice, count the dots and for each dot they make a tally in one of the shapes on just one line. Emphasise that they are making just one mark for each dot on the dice. Ask questions such as: *"How many tallies now on the circles?"* Say *"There were 3 tallies already on the squares and we are adding 2 more. You don't need to count from 1 again, keep the 3 in your head."* Say *"Tamsin, come and make a tally in 5 of the triangles. Is there space for those 5 on the line of circles? How many left to fill in on the squares?"*

 **Starting point: Whole class**

- Look at patterns, such as on clothes and wrapping paper to establish what a pattern is. Ask the children to copy a clapping/word pattern – 'clap, tap knees, clap, tap knees'.
- Make patterns with familiar objects, such as short and tall bottles. *"Tell me about my bottle pattern. Do I need the tall bottle next or the short one?"*

- With the children sitting in a circle, make a pattern with some large shapes (square, triangle, square, triangle) in the middle of the circle. Ask *"What comes next?"* (Repeating patterns with 2D or 3D shapes needs to be covered in separate lessons.) Go around the circle asking each child to put down the next shape. Choose a confident child to start a pattern and ask others to continue it. Draw some patterns on the board and explain the codes for the colours (as on the activity sheets). Draw half a face and show them how to position a mirror to get the whole face.

Group activities

Focus group

Make patterns with strings of beads, each child making a necklace/belt/crown for another child. *"Saphie wants circle, square, circle, square on her crown."* Keep asking *"What comes next?"* With more able children, work with a greater variety of shapes and more complex patterns, for example two

78
©Hopscotch Educational Publishing

developing
Numeracy
Skills

Numeracy
Reception/P1

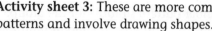

Patterns and puzzles

3-sided shapes then one 4-sided shape, then two 3-sided shapes and so on.

 Teacher Independent Groups

Use the photocopiable activity sheets.

✦ **Activity sheet 1:** These children start with mirrors to explore the patterns (Islamic top right, Greek top left). Let them play and find patterns and talk to each other about what they see. The circle pattern needs black and one colour and the clothes pattern any two colours.

✦ **Activity sheet 2:** This activity has a double yellow pattern in line 2. These children need mirrors for the last part of the sheet and should discuss what

they find. They should count the spots on the bug. The duck and bug aren't symmetrical.

✦ **Activity sheet 3:** These are more complex patterns and involve drawing shapes. The pattern bottom right is Native American. The apple isn't symmetrical, you can't 'see the same'.

✦ *Plenary session*

✦ Let some children from each group show the class what they have done. Talk about what the children using mirrors could see. Say *"Show us how you made a 2 headed duck."* and *"Is this bug the same on both sides of its body?"*

LESSON TWO NUMBER PATTERNS

✦ *Assessment focus*

✦ Can the children recognise patterns in numbers and predict what would come next?

✦ *Resources*

✦ cubes and rods
✦ 100 square and number line

✦ *Oral work and mental calculation*

Patterns

✦ Say some word patterns, *"big bear, little bear, big bear"* and so on. Use the names of shapes to say a pattern, such as *"triangle, square, square, triangle, square, square"*. Move on to looking at number patterns, for example button patterns: *"4 holes, 2 holes, 4 holes"* and so on.

✦ *Starting point: Whole class*

✦ Say *"Some number patterns get bigger and bigger. 1, 2, 3, is getting bigger by one each time. What comes next? How did you know?"*

"2, 4, 6 gets bigger by 2 each time. Can you see the pattern? What comes next?"

✦ Explore other simple number patterns, drawing dots if you want, for example:

   1, 3, 5, 7
   11, 10, 9
   1 add 1 is 2
   2 add 1 is 3
   3 add 1 is 4

Patterns and puzzles

◆ Group activities

Focus group

Choose a number pattern suitable for the group, such as adding 2 to a number, adding in multiples of 10 and subtracting 1 from a number. Ask the children to predict as you circle numbers on the 100 square.

Teacher independent groups

+ **Group 1:** This group should make a staircase pattern with cubes or Cuisenaire rods. Ask "What comes next?" Some children might be able to draw the pattern they have made.

+ **Group 2:** Ask this group to make a pattern with cubes like this: put down 1, then miss a number, put down 3 then miss a number.

+ **Group 3:** Ask these children to start on 1 on the number line or 100 square and count in 2s, circling every second number: 1, 3, 5, 7. They could ask each other questions, such as *"Is 20 in this pattern?"* (No) *"What about 21?"* (Yes) *"What about 31, 41, 51?"*

◆ Plenary session

+ Let children from each group show their patterns, then cover a part of it to ask the group *"What comes next?"*
+ Pattern is so important in maths that it would be helpful to make an interactive display with cubes, teddies, stamper pens and paper strips so that the children can make more patterns.

◆ Further activities

+ Make a pattern bug to predict hidden patterns. Conceal the strips of patterns in a double layer of the wings, then gradually pull out the pattern asking children to predict what will come next.

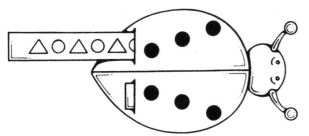

+ You can make a variety of wings for the bug, some symmetrical and some not. *"Are Pattern Bug's wings symmetrical today?"*

+ Let the children explore further with mirrors and identify shapes which are and are not symmetrical. Explore leaves, mini-beasts and other classroom items.
+ Make patterns with sounds and musical instruments that children can join in.
+ Play with kaleidoscopes.

◆ Extension

+ Challenge children to more complex number patterns e.g. start on 13 and count on in 10s.

◆ Support

+ Make a simple pattern each day with buttons, cubes, beads, or print patterns with sponges and 3D shapes.

✦ Patterns ✦

✦ You need a mirror. What do you see?

✦ Make patterns using colours.

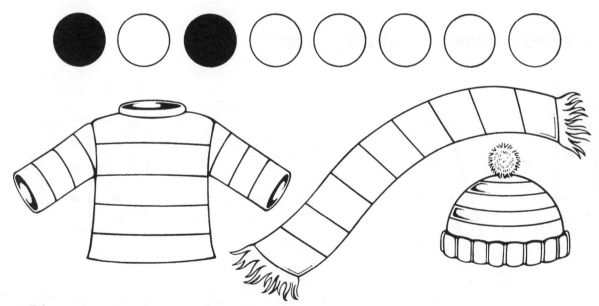

 Use a mirror on other pictures.

Name _____

◆ Patterns ◆

◆ Finish the patterns.

 r red   b blue   y yellow

r   b   r   b   ○   ○   ○

 r   y   y   r   ○   ○   r   ○   ○

◆ Choose colours.

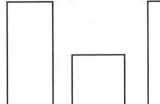

◆ You need a mirror. What do you see?

 Make up patterns with shapes.   △   ○   □

Photocopiable
©Hopscotch Educational Publishing

developing
Numeracy
Skills

✦ **Patterns** ✦

 green    yellow

✦ Finish this pattern.

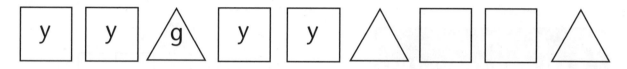

✦ Choose your own colours.

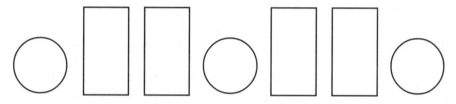

✦ Make a pattern.

✦ You need a mirror. What can you see?

📖 Make patterns with shapes.

Solving problems

✦ Overall learning objectives

✦ Solve simple mathematical problems.
✦ Make predictions.
✦ Use shapes, position, direction and movement.
✦ Use simple data-handling techniques.

LESSON ONE
CAN YOU SOLVE IT?

✦ Assessment focus

✦ Can the children solve simple mathematical problems related to shape (or number)?

✦ Resources

✦ 2D and/or 3D shapes
✦ shape stencils
✦ feely bag

✦ Oral work and mental calculation

Talking about shapes

✦ Show the children four different shapes (use 2D or 3D on different days). Name them and talk about the edges and faces and how one is different from the others. Put them in a feely bag and ask a confident child to come and feel one and describe it to see if everyone can guess the shape.
✦ Play 'guess how many sides'. You hold up a shape, such as a square, and the children immediately shout out the number of sides. Invite one child up to count them.
✦ Make some irregular triangles, four-sided shapes and hexagons, and use seven-, eight- and nine-sided shapes to encourage the children to count and talk about shapes.

✦ Starting point: Whole class

✦ Draw a large grid on the board, at least 3 by 3, such as the one below. Challenge the children to say which items go in which squares on the grid. *"Where does the blue 3-sided shape go?"*

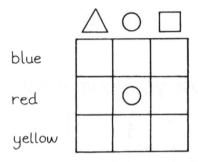

✦ If you think the children need the additional support, you could repeat this on the board using one of the grids for bugs on the activity sheets. Ask *"How do you know that is the right row?"* (*"Because it is a long thin bug with 2 dots"* and so on.)

✦ Group activities

    Focus group

Repeat the starter activity using more 2D shapes. Assess how the children solve the problem and their ability to describe shapes. (Include some irregular shapes.) If you are working with a more able group you could try to do a simple addition square.

+	1	2	3	4
1	2	3	4	5
2	3		5	
3				

Solving problems

 Teacher independent groups

Use the photocopiable activity sheets.

✦ **Activity sheet 1:** The children cut out the bugs, position them on the grid according to the shape of the body, then stick them down. Tell them that there are two bugs that will not fit onto the grid. They should keep these for the plenary session.

✦ **Activity sheet 2:** This is a similar activity to Activity sheet 1. Some bugs will not fit the grid as it is. The ladybird with 4 dots could if there was a row for 4 dots. The 6-sided (hexagonal) bug won't fit at all unless another column is added.

✦ **Activity sheet 3:** For some children you could cut out the squares to simplify the task. (Alternatively, they could draw the bugs in the appropriate place.) Two rectangular bugs are on the sheet, but they need a row created for them. (Clarify that these are also 4-sided, so could go in the same row as the squares.) The 3-sided shapes are all different, but still have 3 sides so they go in

the same row. The 6-sided (hexagonal) and 5-sided (pentagonal) bugs will not fit without rows being created for them on the grid.

✦ **Plenary session**

✦ Ask a child from each group to show their completed sheet. Ask *"How do you know you are right to put that bug in that space?"* Do the others agree? Ask the children who did Activity sheet 1 to identify where on Activity sheet 2 their two spare bugs would fit. Ask someone from each of the other groups to say which bugs would not fit on their grid. Ask *"Could you make your grid larger so you could fit that bug on?"*

✦ Using any of the sheets, ask *"Could I take that bug out of that space and put it somewhere else on this same grid?"* (Usually not, but rectangles and squares could be interchangeable on Activity sheet 3. You might want to say they are all 'rectangles' – shapes with square corners – then identify them as oblongs and squares.)

LESSON TWO HIDE AND SEEK

✦ **Assessment focus**

✦ Can the children solve problems related to position, direction and movement?

✦ **Oral work and mental calculation**

Number bonds of 10

✦ Play 'Superbug whispers'. A child comes out and whispers a number that the others must make up to 10, such as *"3"*, and the rest must whisper back *"7"*. Play this game as often as you can.

✦ **Starting point: Whole class**

✦ Play a hide and seek game. Send two confident children out of the room while you hide a special object somewhere. The children come back in and can only move where the rest of the class tell them to go. *"Take 2 steps forward. Turn left. Go back 1 step"*, and so on until the object is found. Use 'forward', 'back', 'left' and 'right'. (For children with orientation problems put a red dot on the right hand – R for red and R for right.)

Solving problems

◆ Group activities

Focus group

If possible, use a floor robot to give the children as much experience with direction and movement as you can. Say *"Let's drive the robot along this road into the garage."* Ask them to give you directions.

Using a small car, work on words for movement in a similar way. *"The car is going along the road, under the bridge, turning around, going in a circle, stopping next to the teddy"* and so on.

Alternatively, play a 'Where is teddy?' game by putting a small teddy in a variety of places and the children saying where it is, for example *"under/in/ beside the box, next to the brick, to the left of the cup and saucer, on top of the table"* and so on. Assess which position words they need help with.

Teacher independent groups

◆ **Group 1:** This group (which could be split into two smaller groups) should make a building using resources such as bricks, Lego or small world toys and agree where to hide a small object inside it. They should prepare clues to where it is hidden to tell the others at the plenary session.

◆ **Group 2:** This group should agree where to hide an object in the classroom and then each child could draw their own representation of where it is hidden.

◆ **Group 3:** This group could also agree where to hide an object in the classroom and then draw a map or plan of the classroom with the hidden object marked as a cross.

◆ Plenary session

◆ One child from each group should guide the others to where their object is hidden. For example, *"It's in the corner of the back room behind the chair."* Group 2 should explain their pictures: *"We buried it in the sand near the bulldozer"*. One child from Group 3 could be challenged to direct someone from a specific point, such as the door, to where their object is hidden, referring to the plan the group has drawn: *"Go 4 steps forward, go around the table, it is under the book."* (You might not be able to find some things!)

◆ Further activities

◆ Play 'What's in a square?' using faces, buttons or other familiar objects, gradually increasing the size of the grid. With 3D shapes you can use 'has curved faces' and 'doesn't have curved faces', or 'is good for building a tower' and 'isn't good for building a tower' and so on.

◆ How many different ways can you split 5 pence into 2 purses?

◆ A meal must be made of 4 items, choosing from triangular sandwiches and round jam tarts. So you could have 4 sandwiches, or 3 sandwiches and 1 jam tart, or 2 sandwiches and 2 jam tarts and so on.

◆ Will you be able to build a tower with just 10 bricks and make it taller than you?

◆ Who is tallest/oldest in the class?

◆ Extension

◆ A very confident child could be blindfolded and guided (slowly!) across the classroom.

◆ Support

◆ Continue words for position, direction and movement in PE and role play.

Where do the bugs go?

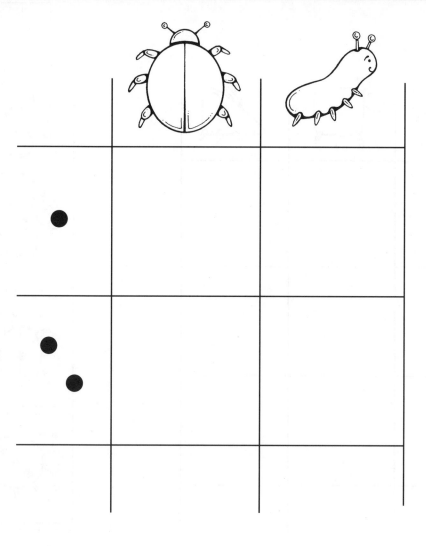

87

◆ Where do the bugs go? ◆

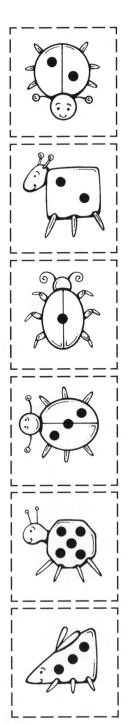

developing **Numeracy Skills**

◆ Where do the bugs go? ◆

developing Numeracy Skills

89

✦ Blue bean throw ✦

once	twice	3 times
1 2 3 4 5 6 7 8 9 10		

developing Numeracy Skills

Name _____

◆ Number line ◆

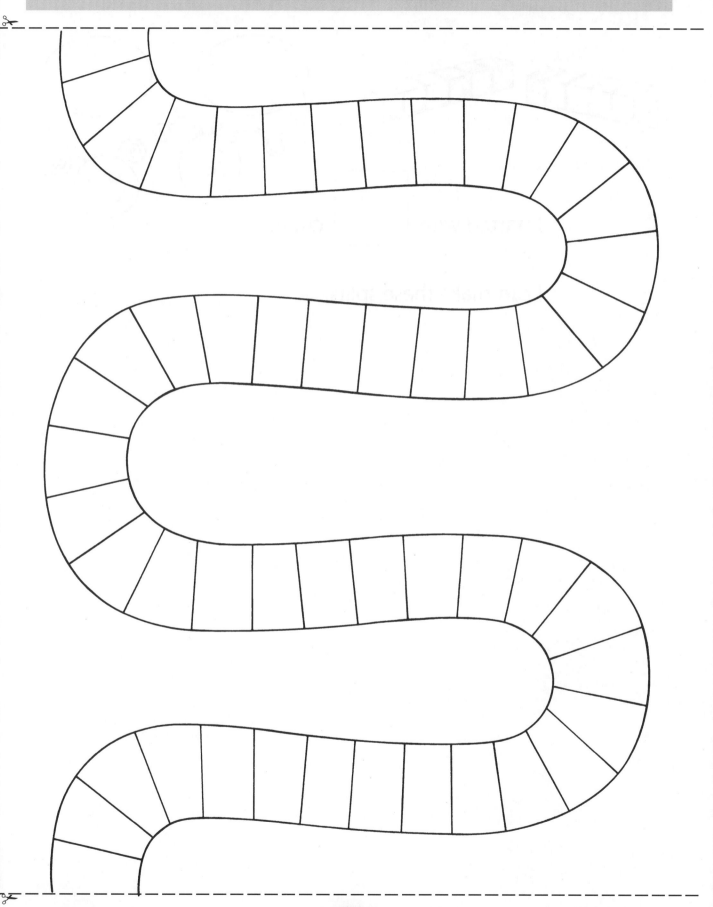

✦ Cube trains ✦

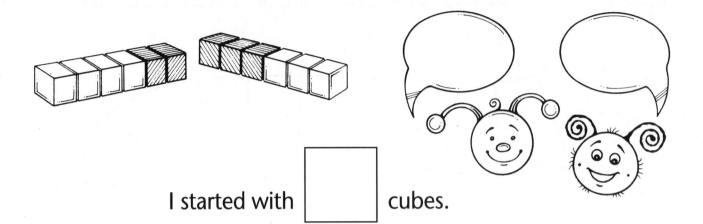

I started with ☐ cubes.

I can make these splits.

◆ Superbug games ◆

1	2	3	4	5	6

developing **Numeracy Skills**

Photocopiable
©Hopscotch Educational Publishing

◆ 3 in a row ◆

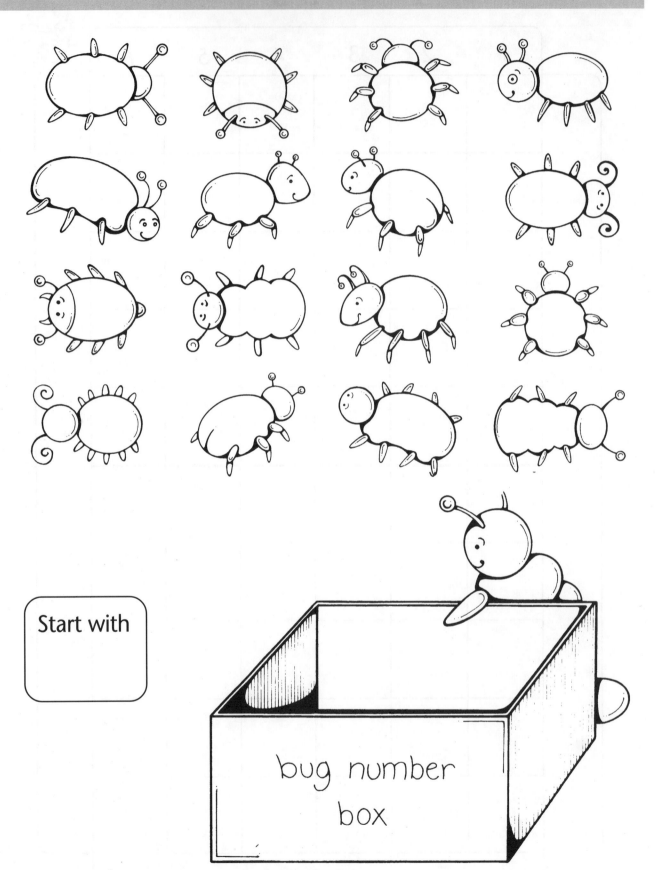

Start with

bug number
box

developing
**Numeracy
Skills**

✦ Assessment ✦

Can talk about more and less.	Can talk about 1st, 2nd, 3rd, last.	Puts the larger number first when adding.	Can separate objects into 2 groups and count, can combine 2 groups.
	Can step along a number line and talk about numbers.	Orders and compares numbers to 10/20.	Mentally adds and subtracts 1 to a number.	
Recites to 20 or more.	Doesn't count from 1 each time.	Can relate numerals to counting.	Makes reasonable estimates.
	Can count a set of objects starting in the middle.	Sees meaning for symbols and records them.	One number word for each count/step.	
Counts reliably a set of objects (1 to 1 correspondence).	Makes one tally for each object.	Knows last number in the count is the number in the set.	Doesn't count objects twice.
	Recites numbers to 3/5/10.	Recognises numbers to 3/5/10.	Knows number remains the same however objects are grouped (conservation).	

Numeracy
Reception/P1

developing
Numeracy Skills

Photocopiable

©Hopscotch Educational Publishing

95

◆ Assessment ◆

developing
**Numeracy
Skills**